METHUEN'S MONOGRAPHS
ON BIOLOGICAL SUBJECTS

General Editor: KENNETH MELLANBY, C.B.E.

THE BIOGENESIS OF MITOCHONDRIA

The Biogenesis of Mitochondria

D. B. ROODYN, M.A., Ph.D.

and

D. WILKIE, B.Sc., Ph.D.

University College London

METHUEN & CO LTD

11 NEW FETTER LANE LONDON EC4

First published in 1968
© *1968 D. B. Roodyn and D. Wilkie*
Printed in Great Britain by
Richard Clay (The Chaucer Press), Ltd.,
Bungay, Suffolk

85·

Distribution in the U.S.A.
by Barnes & Noble, Inc.

Contents

PART II GENETIC AND REGULATORY ASPECTS

Foreword

The last few years has seen a great increase in interest in the question of the mechanism of biogenesis of mitochondria. Stimulated by the discovery of mitochondrial DNA, research in this subject is now in a phase of rapid expansion, and there is much current experimental work on mitochondrial genetics, the electron microscopy of mitochondrial formation, the isolation and characterization of RNA and DNA in mitochondrial fractions, the mechanism of mitochondrial formation and the mechanism of mitochondrial protein synthesis. In addition, there is an increased awareness of the more theoretical aspects of the problem, with much discussion on possible theories of mitochondrial evolution, cellular mechanisms for mitochondrial assembly, and the interaction of nuclear and cytoplasmic genetic systems in the formation of cyctplasmic organelles.

In such an atmosphere of rapid advance, we have been reluctant to present a detailed review of the literature in a subject which ranges over the whole of biology, and which changes from month to month. Instead, we hope to indicate to the reader the lines of investigation which are being pursued at the moment, and the major findings that have been obtained recently. The book is intended for advanced undergraduates in biology, as well as the specialist, and we have found it convenient to present it in two parts, the first showing the approach of the biochemical cytologist, and the second that of the geneticist. However, the reader will see that the overlap and interconnexion between these two approaches are quite considerable, and we hope that our joint effort will help to bring a more unified approach to the problem.

We have been rather hesitant to propound rigid theories at this stage. The avenues opened by recent advances are so exciting, and the prospects that a clear picture will emerge in the near future so promising, that there seems little point in making guesses at this stage, however well inspired. In the meantime, we present this 'interim report', and await further results with interest.

July 1967

PART ONE

Biochemical and Cytological Aspects

CHAPTER ONE

Mitochondrial Nucleic Acids

Mitochondrial DNA

The existence of cytoplasmic genetic systems has been established for many years (see Wilkie, 1964), and Chayen, for example, had argued for some years that considerable amounts of DNA are present in the cytoplasm of certain plant cells (for a recent account of cytoplasmic DNA see Gahan and Chayen, 1965). The presence of DNA in the cytoplasm of the amphibian oocyte had also been known for some time (see Deuchar, 1966). (Most of this is in fact due to mitochondrial DNA; Dawid, 1966.) By a combination of autoradiography and the Feulgen stain, Chèvremont and his colleagues demonstrated the presence of DNA in the mitochondria of tissue culture cells in the late 1950s (Chèvremont, Bassleer, and Baekeland, 1961). It was also true that small amounts of DNA were found in isolated mitochondrial fractions, prepared by 'standard' centrifugal fractionation in sucrose. However, these amounts (1–5 per cent of the total DNA) were usually ascribed to nuclear contamination.

Perhaps the subject had to wait for the development of more rigorous methods for the isolation and characterization of DNA before these findings could be exploited. In particular, sucrose density-gradient analysis and thermal denaturation studies provide a way of distinguishing nuclear and mitochondrial DNA. Thus when Nass and Nass demonstrated in 1963 that the fibrils which they and other workers had previously observed in the matrix of mitochondria were, in fact, fibrils of DNA, many research groups began to look for a specific DNA in various mitochondrial fractions. Nass, Nass, and Afzelius (1965) showed the occurrence of DNA in mitochondria from a wide range of cell types and, as will be described below, direct biochemical studies have confirmed the universal occurrence of mitochondrial DNA (MDNA).

The task of establishing that the very small amount of DNA found in the mitochondrial fraction (often much less than 1 per cent of the total DNA) is not due to nuclear contamination at first appeared rather daunting. Resistance to DNase (which presumably could not penetrate the mitochondrial membrane) was taken as a first check against nuclear contamination. Fortunately the DNA isolated from mitochondria was soon found to have several distinguishing features, and when it was established that it is in fact *circular* (Kroon, Borst, Van Bruggen, and Ruttenberg, 1966; Nass, 1966; Sinclair and Stevens, 1966) there was no doubt that MDNA existed as a separate type of DNA.

It should be pointed out that it has recently been established that the low-molecular weight DNA associated with yeast lactate dehydrogenase (cytochrome b_2) is in fact an artifact, caused by binding of DNA fragments to the enzyme during purification. Since cytochrome b_2 is localized in mitochondria in yeast, there had been the possibility that this DNA had some biological function (see Wilkie, 1964, for a discussion of this).

General properties of MDNA

Occurence of MDNA. Nass et al. (1965) examined mitochondria from about sixty different organisms. In each case they observed the characteristic DNA fibrils lying in the matrix. The occurrence of intramitochondrial fibrils of one sort or another has been described frequently (e.g. Mugnaini, 1964a; Schuster, 1965), and it is now likely that many of these, in fact, consist of DNA.

MDNA has now been isolated from mitochondria prepared from yeast, Tetrahymena, several amphibians, a range of plant tissues, and from various tissues in a range of different animals, including chick, pigeon, mouse, rat, guinea-pig, lamb. There is thus no reasonable doubt that MDNA is a universal characteristic of all mitochondria.

Buoyant densities. A striking feature of the various MDNA's isolated until now is that they resemble each other more closely than the nuclear DNA's of the cells from which the mitochondria were isolated. While it is not true to say that MDNA is identical, whatever its source, there are nevertheless homologies between MDNA's in large groups of organisms. For example, the buoyant densities of mammalian MDNA's fall within the range 1·700-1·704, whereas the nuclear DNA's from the same animals show a wide range. Also the nuclear DNA's in various plants examined by Suyama and Bonner (1966) ranged in buoyant density from 1·688 to 1·692, whereas the corresponding MDNA's all had densities of 1·706. Indeed, these results were so consistent that Kroon *et al.* (1966) were forced to question the observation of Kalf and Grece (1966) that lamb-heart MDNA had a density of 1·714. They concluded that, in fact, true MDNA in this animal has a density of 1·703 (i.e. it falls within the range found for mammalian MDNA), and the DNA of density 1·714 is in fact a minor component of nuclear DNA (so-called 'satellite DNA').

Confusion of MDNA and 'satellite DNA' occurred in some of the initial work. However, it is now reasonably certain that the minor component often seen in nuclear DNA is not MDNA. For example, the satellite DNA in mouse liver that has a buoyant density of 1·690 is completely absent from purified mouse-liver MDNA (density, 1·699; Sinclair and Stevens, 1966). The question of the relationship between MDNA and satellite DNA in yeast is still somewhat confused, however (see Chapter Six).

Thermal denaturation and renaturation. There is little doubt that MDNA exists in the double-stranded form. When double-stranded DNA is heated, at a certain temperature the double helical structure collapses because of rupture of hydrogen bonds, and a random arrangement of the strands results. This 'denaturation' of the molecule is accompanied by a characteristic increase in absorbance (or 'hyperchromic effect'), at 260 mμ, for example, and this effect can be used to determine the 'melting temperature' or 'T_m' of the molecule. The T_m's of various MDNA's have been examined, and generally differ from the T_m of the corresponding nuclear DNA. However, a most striking property of MDNA is its rapid rate of 'renaturation' (Borst and Ruttenberg, 1966). Normally, DNA takes a long time to recover from thermal denaturation, the recovery process being indicated by a slow fall in absorbance of the denatured DNA. MDNA, however, renatures rapidly and fully recovers its hyperchromicity. An example of the great difference in the behaviour of MDNA is shown in Fig. 1.

The ready renaturation of MDNA has now been observed by several workers and appears to be a characteristic property. Its significance is that it indicates that MDNA is *more homogeneous in its base composition* than nuclear DNA. Thus viral DNA and synthetic polynucleotides renature far more easily than the nuclear DNA of higher plants and animals. Presumably there is a relationship between the complexity of DNA and the specificity of its biological role. Thus if a DNA is only codes for the synthesis of one or two proteins it would be more homogeneous in base composition than a DNA coding for hundreds of

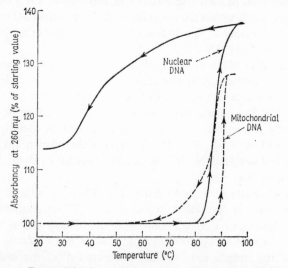

FIG. I Reversible thermal changes in mitochondrial DNA
Nuclear and mitochondrial DNA from chick liver were heated and then cooled. Note that MDNA recovers its hyperchromic properties immediately and completely, but nuclear DNA does not
(From Borst *et al.*, 1967, with kind permission of the authors.)

proteins. For example, Du Buy, Mattern, and Riley (1966) found that MDNA from mouse brain renatured more rapidly than the corresponding nuclear DNA. However, DNA isolated from the kinetoplast of *Leishmanii enrietti* renatured even more rapidly. These workers then suggested that kinetoplast DNA is less complex than mouse MDNA because it has a more specific function (i.e. it encodes far fewer proteins).

Circularity of MDNA. These indications of fundamental qualitative differences between nuclear and mitochondrial DNA were fully confirmed by the demonstration of circularity of MDNA.

It has been known for some time that the linkage map in bacteria is circular, and indeed circular DNA molecules have been isolated from bacteria, and viruses.

Circular DNA molecules have now been isolated from mitochondria of many different types of tissue, and it is interesting that they all appear to have an average length of about 5 μ. Nass (1966) studied the circular DNA of mitochondria from mouse fibroblasts. Mitochondria were osmotically lysed and the released DNA was immediately absorbed

NATIVE   DENATURED

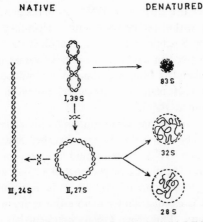

FIG. 2 Various forms of mitochondrial DNA
(S: sedimentation coefficients)
(From Kroon et al., 1966, with kind permission of the authors)

on to a film of cytochrome c. Electron microscopy then showed the presence of circular molecules, confirming that circularity in purified MDNA is not an artifact caused by re-annealing of linear chains during isolation. Nass also observed that there may be two to six rings of DNA per mitochondrion. This may be of some relevance to the problem of the apparently limited coding capacity of MDNA (see below). Nass et al. (1965) had previously found that the highly branched mitochondria in chick heart cells appeared to contain DNA fibres in each branch. This suggests that MDNA may have a limited 'range of action'.

Several other groups have recently demonstrated circularity of MDNA. It appears that after isolation MDNA can be present in various conformations. Thus the circles may be open, twisted, 'hypertwisted', or tightly aggregated. Linear fragments are also present. All these factors would affect the sedimentation properties of the DNA (as shown in Fig. 2). The biological significance of such multiplicity of conformation is not yet certain, but it would be most interesting if corresponding changes occurred *in vivo*.

Molecular weight and amount per mitochondrion. If it is assumed that there is only one molecule of DNA per mitochondrion, the amount of DNA per mitochondrion can be used as an estimate of its molecular weight. Values for the amount of DNA per mitochondrion, however, appeared to vary within rather wide limits, depending on the source. As pointed out by Sinclair and Stevens (1966), if the DNA per mitochondrion is expressed in daltons, one obtains values in the literature for various mitochondria from 2 million to 100 million. In particular, the DNA content of plant mitochondria appears to be very high (Suyama and Bonner, 1966).

However, mitochondria appear to contain multiple filaments of DNA, and as mentioned above, it is now certain that they contain several rings of DNA. The high DNA values found in some mitochondria are therefore probably to be due to the presence of a larger number of rings, rather than a larger molecule of MDNA. It is most fortunate that the fact that MDNA is circular allows us to estimate its molecular weight with some certainty. Thus Nass (1966) assumed that a 1μ length of DNA had a mass of 1·92 million daltons. A circular molecule of length about 5μ would thus have a molecular weight of about 10 million. The values given for the molecular weight of MDNA by various workers fall within the range of 9–11 million.

Base composition and sequences in MDNA. We are no doubt at the very early stages of some most exciting work on this problem. All the indications are that MDNA is a rather homogeneous molecule, and it may well be a useful 'model substance' for examining the structure of DNA. The base composition (usually expressed as '% G C', i.e. the per cent of the total bases that are cytidine + guanine) is related to the buoyant density of DNA. Some of the early suggestions that MDNA had a greatly different buoyant density from nuclear DNA raised the hope that the base compositions of the two DNA's may be grossly different. However, it now appears likely that most species of MDNA have, in fact, densities that are not very different from the corresponding nuclear DNA.

Of course it is premature to hope for a rigorous chemical determination of base sequences in a molecule of molecular weight 10 million. However, a subtle method available for study of base sequence is the determination of 'nearest-neighbour frequencies'. In this a statistical evaluation is made of the frequency in which various nucleotides occur next to each other in the polynucleotide chain. Recently Cummins, Rusch, and Evans (1967) have compared the nearest-neighbour frequencies of dinucleotides ending with guanylic acid in nuclear and MDNA. The organism studied was the slime mould *Physarum polycephalum*. The value obtained for MDNA with the dinucleotide CpG (cytidylyl guanylate) was very near the value one would expect for a random distribution of nucleotides. However, the same dinucleotide occurred in nuclear DNA with a frequency much less than that expected from a random distribution. Other dinucleotides also showed marked differences in their nearest-neighbour frequencies in the two DNA's. (Cummins *et al.* makes the interesting comment that the pattern nearest-neighbour frequencies observed in MDNA is similar to that observed in bacterial DNA's – see Chapter Four.)

There is thus no doubt that MDNA represents a distinct species of DNA different from nuclear DNA in a number of important qualitative and quantitative aspects. These observations thus parallel the recent discoveries of chloroplast DNA (see, e.g., Gibor and Granick, 1964; Shipp, Kieras, and Hazelkorn, 1965).

Intramitochondrial location of MDNA

This is an important question for our understanding of the precise mechanism of mitochondrial biogenesis. Nass *et al.* (1965) observed that most of the DNA fibrils appear to lie in the matrix. However, there were often frequent fine fibrillar connexions to the cristae or to the inner membrane. Attachment between strands of MDNA and pieces of mitochondrial membrane was also often observed by Nass (1966) during isolation of MDNA.

Apart from such electron-microscope observations, there are other indications of an association between MDNA and the membrane. Kroon (1965) prepared sub-mitochondrial particles by digitonin lysis of

B

beef-heart mitochondria, and found that they were enriched in DNA. These particles were also very active in amino-acid incorporation, and studies with actinomycin D indicated that DNA was involved in this process. The possible role of MDNA in mitochondrial protein synthesis is discussed more fully below (Chapter Three,) and it is not at all unlikely from present evidence that DNA, RNA, and the protein synthesizing system of mitochondria lie in a close relationship to the mitochondrial membrane.

The Biosynthesis of MDNA

There has been recent evidence that isolated mitochondria can synthesize DNA. Haldar, Freeman, and Work (1966) showed that isolated liver and tumour mitochondria can incorporate ^{3}H-thymidine and ^{14}C-uracil into an acid insoluble polymer that is presumably DNA. In view of the control that thyroid hormones have over mitochondrial protein synthesis (Chapter Three), it is most interesting that these workers also found that this incorporation is greater in mitochondria from animals treated with thyroid hormones. Wintersberger (1966a) has demonstrated the presence of DNA polymerase in isolated yeast mitochondria, by following the incorporation of ^{3}H-deoxy ATP into an acid-insoluble product which was then characterized as DNA. The incorporation is partly inhibited by actinomycin D, and by mitomycin C, a typical inhibitor of DNA synthesis.

The demonstration of the ability of isolated mitochondria to synthesize DNA is thus an important advance in our understanding of the mechanism of mitochondrial inheritance. Indeed, labelling experiments *in vivo* have not only confirmed that synthesis of MDNA takes place but also indicate that there is a certain degree of autonomy in this synthesis (i.e. it is not precisely in phase with nuclear DNA synthesis).

Thus Parsons (1965) followed the labelling of mitochondrial (basal body) DNA in *Tetrahymena pyriformis* by labelling with ^{3}H-thymidine followed by autoradiography. He followed the level of radioactivity in mitochondria over several cell generations and concluded that MDNA was passed on to daughter cells without being broken down. This indication of stability of MDNA during cell division is an important point when considering the genetic autonomy of the mitochondrion. Neubert, Helge, and Bass (1965) have reported labelling of mitochondrial DNA *in vivo* with labelled thymidine and shown that the synthesis of MDNA is not exactly in phase with that of nuclear DNA. Using the slime mould *Physarum polycephalum*, Guttes, Hanawalt, and Guttes (1967) have recently shown that ^{3}H-thymidine is incorporated into MDNA throughout the mitotic cycle, with no evidence of periodicity. Thus, although the DNA in each individual mitochondrion may be made in a periodic manner, the total amount of MDNA in the whole mitochondrial population is clearly not made in 'phase' with nuclear DNA.

The mechanism of replication of MDNA during cell division has been studied in detail by Reich and Luck (1966), using *Neurospora crassa*. They attempted to repeat the fundamental and well-known experiment of Meselson and Stahl (1958) which had established the 'semi-conservative' mechanism of replication of DNA in *E. coli*, as would be expected from the Watson–Crick–Wilkins model. Reich and Luck grew Neurospora in an ^{15}N-medium, and then transferred the labelled cells to an ^{14}N-medium. After one, two, or three cell doublings, the mitochondria were isolated and their MDNA analysed by density-gradient centrifuging on CsCl. Although it was not possible to demonstrate ^{14}N, mixed, and ^{15}N labelled strands in the native DNA after one cell cycle, if the DNA was heat-denatured it could be shown quite clearly that *intact ^{15}N-labelled strands* had been passed from one generation to the next. The results were not as clear-cut as with *E. coli* because there appeared to be a considerable pool of DNA precursors in the mitochondria, which was only slowly diluted by the added isotope. Thus it was not until the third generation that the density-gradient centrifuging showed conclusively that a hybrid strand had been formed. However, Reich and Luck's work shows that there is little doubt that the semi-conservative mechanism of replication operates for MDNA.

There is thus reasonably good evidence that mitochondria are able to synthesize DNA, and that MDNA is stable from generation to generation. (Facultative anaerobes among micro-organisms are the only likely exceptions to this stability – see Chapter Six.) These two facts are powerful indications of at least some autonomy of the genetic system involved in mitochondrial replication. However, as is discussed more fully elsewhere (Chapter Six), there is good evidence for the existence of considerable *nuclear* control of the formation and assembly of mitochondrial constituents. It is not certain at the moment whether MDNA is entirely made in mitochondria, or is in fact a copy of part of the nuclear genome. Recently Du Buy and Riley (1967) have attempted to determine the extent to which MDNA is a copy of nuclear DNA by direct hybridization experiments. They found that nuclear fragments could reassociate with mitochondrial DNA, although about half as effectively as with intact nuclear DNA. This would indicate that there is considerable homology between the two types of DNA, although it is not yet known whether the entire sequence of bases in MDNA is in fact found in the corresponding nuclear DNA.

The biological function of MDNA

The most obvious role to assign to MDNA is that it is the repository of the genetic information required for the synthesis of the mitochondrion. Its ubiquity, stability through cell divisions, and formation in isolated mitochondria all suggest that it represents an autonomous genetic system. (The relationship between nuclear genes and plastid DNA is discussed in a stimulating article by Gibor and Granick, 1964.) However, there is considerable evidence, both biochemical and genetic, that MDNA does not, and indeed *cannot*, code for the synthesis of all mitochondrial proteins. The genetic evidence and the relationship of MDNA with the 'ρ particle' is discussed fully in Chapter Six. The limited activity of isolated mitochondria with respect to protein synthesis, and the evidence for non-mitochondrial synthesis of certain proteins, is also discussed in detail in Chapters Two and Three. At this point it will be useful to discuss evidence that is derived from the properties of MDNA itself.

The fortunate discovery that MDNA is a circular model allows us to make some estimate of its potential 'coding capacity'. Since it is now reasonably well established that at least three nucleotides are required to specify the position in a polypeptide chain of a single amino acid, one can calculate from the molecular weight of MDNA the maximum number of amino acids whose position can be determined. Thus for a molecular weight of 10–11 million (corresponding to about 15,000 base pairs) the maximum genetic information available would encode for a sequence of about one-third of this number, i.e. 5,000 amino acids. Sinclair and Stevens (1966) calculate that this would be equivalent to one protein of molecular weight about 580,000, or about thirty proteins of molecular weight 20,000. Another way of expressing this result is to say that the maximum weight of protein that can be encoded for by *one molecule* of MDNA is about 600,000.

We have to consider whether such a situation is consistent with the view that the sequences for the synthesis of *all* mitochondrial proteins are encoded by MDNA. Lehninger (1964), in his excellent book *The Mitochondrion*, gave the *minimum* particle weight of the respiratory assembly as 1,350,000. This included NADH dehydrogenase, succinate dehydrogenase, and the cytochromes. If one also included various coupling factors and respiratory enzymes (e.g. pyridine nucleotide transhydrogenase), one arrived at a figure of 1,830,000. However, these values exclude many important mitochondrial enzymes, such as the tricarboxylic acid cycle enzymes, aminotransferases, various enzymes involved in protein, RNA and DNA synthesis, and a large number of 'miscellaneous' enzymes. (For a recent survey of the range of metabolic activities of the mitochondrion, see Roodyn, 1967.) These considerations also exclude the non-protein components of the mitochondrion, in particular lipids and the various species of mitochondrial RNA. Thus Sinclair and Stevens (1966) point out that if the nucleotide sequence of RNA ribosomal and transfer RNA is specified by MDNA, 7,000–10,000 base pairs would be required (i.e. one-half to two-thirds of the total coding capacity).

As mentioned above, it is clear that mitochondria can contain more than one molecule of MDNA, and may in fact contain several. If one therefore assumes that several different species of MDNA exist, it may therefore be possible to increase the coding capacity. However, all the current evidence points to MDNA being a rather homogeneous molecule. Also the DNA content of some mitochondria (e.g. from Neurospora) is only about 12 million daltons (Luck and Reich, 1964), so that at least in these cases we can rule out the presence of several species of MDNA. In a detailed analysis of this problem, Borst, Kroon, and Ruttenberg (1967) suggest that the presence of several molecules of DNA per mitochondrion may be due to doubling of DNA occurring before mitochondrial division or budding, or it may result from fusion of mitochondria. They also conclude that the maximum coding capacity in the DNA in each mitochondrion is for about 5,000 amino acids. Taken with other evidence in this book, it is thus reasonable to conclude from present information that *MDNA only encodes for a limited proportion of the total mitochondrial structure.*

Mitochondrial RNA

Evidence for presence of RNA in mitochondria

Recent evidence has made it likely that at least some of the rather small amount of RNA found in mitochondrial fractions is truly mitochondrial. Many workers have found that the RNA in the mitochondrial fraction appears to be labelled *in vivo* at a different rate to the microsomal RNA. If a ^{14}C-labelled microsomal fraction is added to a mitochondrial fraction it can be completely washed out after three washings. However, even after five washings there are still significant amounts of RNA in the mitochondrial fraction (Roodyn, Reis, and Work, 1961). Levels of mitochondrial and microsomal RNA in liver appear to behave somewhat differently after thyroid hormone treatment of the whole animal (Roodyn, Freeman, and Tata, 1965). It has also been found generally that RNA in the mitochondrial fraction is quite resistant to the action of ribonuclease (Roodyn, 1966a; Humm and Humm, 1966). Part of the resistance to RNase is no doubt due to impermeability of the mitochondrial membrane to the enzyme. However, even the RNA in isolated mitochondrial membrane fragments is remarkably resistant to RNase (Roodyn, 1966a).

The most convincing work on this question has been done recently by Barnett and Brown (1967). Using highly purified mitochondria from *Neurospora crassa*, they demonstrated that RNA closely followed cytochrome oxidase on sucrose density gradients (Fig. 3). As will be discussed more fully below, there is now some evidence to suggest that mitochondrial RNA has different species (in terms of S values) to microsomal RNA. It also is likely that mitochondrial ribosomes are qualitatively different from non-mitochondrial cytoplasmic ribosomes. There is also strong evidence for the existence of a specific RNA polymerase in mitochondria, and the massive information on mitochondrial amino-acid incorporation argues strongly in favour of the presence of RNA.

Nevertheless, the technical difficulties of distinguishing mitochondrial RNA from contaminant RNA are still very great, and one would be advised to treat current work in this field with a certain amount of caution at the moment.

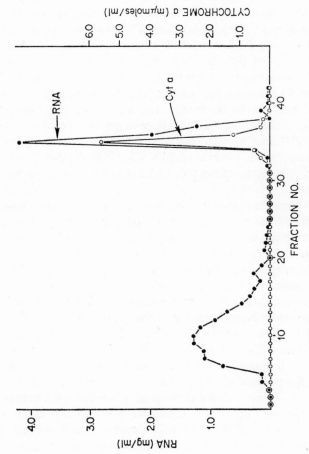

FIG. 3 RNA in mitochondria from *Neurospora crassa*
Mitochondria were analysed by sucrose gradient zonal centrifugation
(From Barnett and Brown, 1967, with kind permission of the authors)

Properties of RNA and ribosomes in mitochondria

Wintersberger (1966b) isolated three species of RNA from yeast mitochondria that had been purified by density-gradient centrifuging. The species were 23 S, 16 S, 4 S. The two larger molecules corresponded to the sub-units of ribosomal RNA and the 4 S species corresponded to RNA. Wintersberger showed that the SRNA fraction was, in fact, amino-acid acceptor RNA comparable to transfer RNA in the cytoplasm. He also used pulse-labelling experiments to demonstrate an RNA species similar to messenger RNA. The values of 23 S and 16 S indicate that the ribosomal unit was similar to the 70 S bacterial ribosome rather than the 80 S ribosome found in all the cytoplasm of yeast and all other eukaryotic cells. Rogers, Preston, Titchener, and Linnane (1967) have recently extended this finding, however, and have demonstrated the presence of 16·2 S and 24·6 S RNA in yeast cytoplasmic* ribosomes, and 12·7 S, 17·8 S, and 22·4 S RNA in yeast mitochondria.

Recently Barnett and Brown (1967) and Barnett, Brown, and Epler (1967) have demonstrated the presence of transfer RNA (tRNA) species for eighteen amino acids in purified mitochondria from *Neurospora crassa*. There appear to be specific phenyl alanyl-, aspartyl-, and leucyl-tRNA species in the mitochondria. The phenyl alanyl-tRNA is present in mitochondria in rather high concentrations. The corresponding activating enzymes also appear to be specifically present in the mitochondria and different from the equivalent cytoplasmic enzymes. The isolation of well-defined RNA species from mammalian mitochondria has proved to be rather difficult, partly because of easier contamination with fragments of the endoplasmic reticulum, and also because of the presence of ribonuclease in the preparations (often in contaminant lysosomes). Thus studies on mitochondrial RNA from rat liver have not yet yielded very conclusive answers. It is generally found that ribosomes of the cytoplasm of nucleated cells have RNA species of 16–18 S for the small sub-unit, and 25–30 S for the large. Bacterial ribosomes contain 16 S and 23 S ribosomal RNA, however. (For a full account of the various RNA species in ribosomes see Petermann, 1964.) The results with mitochondrial RNA are somewhat

* We use the term 'cytoplasmic' as a concise form of 'non-mitochondrial and cytoplasmic', i.e. as distinct from nuclear.

confusing at the moment, but in general there are good indications that mitochondrial RNA contains components that resemble the RNA species of bacterial ribosomes.

The question of the intramitochondrial localization of RNA is important. Presumably the 4 S (soluble) RNA species would be present in the soluble phase of the mitochondrian. In fact, the bulk of mitochondrial RNA is insoluble, with only about 10 per cent being easily extracted, for example, by dilute buffers. During sub-fractionation of liver mitochondria that had been disrupted with neutral detergents, the bulk of the RNA was found in an 'RNA–lipoprotein complex' associated with the mitochondrial membrane (Roodyn, 1962). It proved to be very difficult to obtain the ribonucleoprotein free of phospholipid, and even after extensive detergent treatment, the RNA:protein ratio of the residue was very far from the 1:1 expected for ribosomes. (Good preparations of ribosomes from mitochondria have only been isolated very recently – see below.) Several other workers have found that mitochondrial RNA is concentrated in the membrane fraction after sub-fractionation (e.g. Kroon, 1965). At the moment we cannot be certain whether this corresponds to a fortuitous co-sedimentation of ribosomes and membrane fragments, or whether the RNA is indeed integrated into the membrane structure in some specific way.

There have been several reports recently of ribosomes (or perhaps one should say ribosome-like particles) being observed in electron micrographs. Haldar, Freeman, and Work (1967) found that after treatment of ascites cells with ribonuclease, cytoplasmic ribosomes largely disappeared, but ribosome-like structures could be clearly seen in the mitochondria. Intramitochondrial ribosomes have also been seen by André and Marinozzi (1965) and a variety of other workers. (For further references to these observations see O'Brien and Kalf, 1967.) Apart from their size, which is generally smaller than cytoplasmic ribosomes, the particles were taken to be ribosomes primarily because of their sensitivity to ribonuclease and of their staining properties. They can be clearly distinguished from the so-called 'stalked bodies' and from the 'dense granules' (see Roodyn, 1967, for a description of these).

There have been recent attempts to isolate these ribosomes. As mentioned above, some of the earlier preparations of mitochondrial 'ribosomes' were probably heavily contaminated with membrane fragments.

Recently more detailed studies have been made, however. Elaev (1967) isolated ribosomes from rat-heart mitochondria. The ribosomes contained three main components; 83, 63, and 45 S. They thus resembled ribosomes in the microsomal fraction. However, it was unlikely that the ribosomes were in fact derived from the endoplasmic reticulum, since Elaev washed the mitochondria very thoroughly; he also points out that the endoplasmic reticulum is poorly developed in muscle. Nevertheless, the danger of microsomal contamination is very clear. Rabinowitz, de Salle, Sinclair, Stirewalt, and Swift (1966) attempted to eliminate microsomal contamination by treating the mitochondria with ribonuclease and then purifying them on a sucrose density gradient. Again, the ribosomes isolated from these preparations appeared to be similar to microsomal ribosomes.

In a recent careful study of the problem, O'Brien and Kalf (1967) took great care to eliminate microsomal contamination by extensive washing of the mitochondria and repeated purification through sucrose gradients. They also monitored their preparations with electron microscopy, and followed the level of added radioactive microsomal fractions during the washing. They were able to isolate purified mitochondrial ribosomes in low yield and study their properties. The surprising, and most interesting, finding was that the ribosomes appeared to have a sedimentation coefficient of 55 S (i.e. the results differed from those of Elaev, and Rabinowitz $et\ al.$). In a review on ribosomes, Elson (1967) gives the following 'rounded' S values for bacterial ribosomes as 100 S (dimer), 70 S (monomer), and 50 S and 30 S (sub-units). Non-bacterial particles are 120 S (dimer), 80 S (monomer) and 60 S and 40 S (sub-units). Since one should not take these figures too precisely, one could see that the values reported for Elaev, for example (83, 54, and 45 S), probably corresponded to the normal monomer and two sub-units of mammalian ribosomes.

The finding of 55 S ribosomes could mean that these corresponded to the 54 S ribosomal fraction of Elaev, i.e. they were a sub-unit of the 'microsomal'-type ribosome. However, O'Brien and Kalf believe this to be very unlikely. They showed that under their conditions the microsomal ribosomes appeared to be quite stable, and did not break down into sub-units. Also the 55 S particle appeared as a single major peak, with the sign of an equivalent amount of the other expected sub-unit.

Even more convincing was the observation that *only* the 55 S ribosomes became labelled when mitochondria were incubated *in vitro* with radio-active leucine, in the presence of microsomal fractions. Also the diameter of the isolated ribosomes (145 Å) corresponded well with the reported values from electron micrographs intramitochondrial ribosomes (100–150 Å) and were significantly less than the diameter of microsome ribosomes (190 Å).

On the basis of the evidence so far, it appears, therefore, that mitochondria contained ribosomes that are even smaller than bacterial ribosomes (70 S monomer), and are probably 55–60 S monomers. It is most interesting that similar S values have been reported for chloroplast ribosomes (Sissakian, Filippovich, Svetailo, and Aliyev, 1965), so that all plastids may have similar types of ribosome. More recently Stutz and Noll (1967) have made high-resolution centrifugal analyses of plant cells, and confirmed conclusively that cytoplasmic polysomes contain 80 S monomers, whereas the chloroplasts contain polysomes made up of 70 S monomers.

Biosynthesis of mitochondrial RNA

There have been various reports of incorporation into RNA *in vivo* of various RNA precursors in a number of tissues. Also incorporation of a variety of RNA precursors into mitochondrial RNA after incubation of mitochondria *in vitro* has been reported by several workers. Neubert and Helge (1965) showed that ^{14}C-ATP, GTP, and UTP could be incorporated *in vitro*. It was interesting that if the mitochondria were intact, it was difficult to show dependence on added nucleotides. However, if the mitochondria were swollen, so as to become more permeable, this dependence could be demonstrated. These observations were used to show that the activity was not due to contamination with nuclear RNA polymerase. A similar conclusion was reached by Saccone, Gadaleta, and Quagliariello (1967), using atractyloside as an inhibitor.

Neubert and Helge also showed that in the swollen mitochondria the incorporation was inhibited by actinomycin C. This strongly suggested that the incorporation was due to a DNA-dependent RNA polymerase. Neubert, Helge, and Merker (1965) extended their studies to mitochondria from a variety of animals. It is most interesting that they found their system was also inhibited by the addition of acriflavin (see Chapter

Six on petite induction). DNA-dependent RNA polymerase has also been demonstrated in rat-liver mitochondria (Wintersberger, 1964), lamb-heart mitochondria (Kalf, 1964), and mitochondria from *Neurospora crassa* (Luck and Reich, 1964). As with amino-acid incorporation, the question of bacterial contamination is important in these systems, and Kroon, Saccone, and Botman (1967) have recently demonstrated incorporation of ^{14}C-ATP into rat-liver mitochondria isolated under sterile conditions.

There thus seems little doubt that isolated mitochondria can synthesize RNA on a DNA template. One would presume at this stage that the template is in fact MDNA, and no doubt work in the near future will define the radioactive products with greater precision. It would be most interesting to know the sedimentation constant of the newly labelled RNA and whether the enzyme is responsible for the synthesis of SRNA and ribosomal RNA. It is very significant that mitochondrial RNA polymerase appears to be involved in the amino-acid incorporation system. Kalf (1964) showed that this system was inhibited by actinomycin D, and concluded that protein synthesis in the mitochondrion is dependent on a continual synthesis of RNA by RNA polymerase. Kroon (1965) reached a similar conclusion, and found a close association in sub-mitochondrial preparations between DNA, RNA polymerase, and amino-acid incorporation.

Functions of mitochondrial RNA
We are at the beginning of an exciting phase of research into the biosynthetic properties of mitochondria. It would not be unreasonable to propose at the moment that the mitochondrion contains a complete protein-synthesizing apparatus, analogous in all its major properties to that in the intact cell (see Chapter Three). Genetic information encoded in MDNA is replicated by means of mitochondrial DNA polymerase. Transcription occurs by the action of mitochondrial RNA polymerase. One would presume that a form of messenger RNA is thus synthesized, and this then interacts with mitochondrial ribosomes and amino-acyl–SRNA complexes to form protein. However, there are still many unanswered questions in the above scheme. What is the nature of mitochondrial messenger RNA? Where are mitochondrial ribosomes and SRNA made? Are there polysomes in mitochondria? How are the ribo-

somes attached to the membrane, if at all? Is the mechanism of protein biosynthesis on mitochondrial ribosomes identical to that in the 'microsomal' system, or does it have special features?

Some of these questions are being answered at the moment. For example, Humm and Humm (1966) carried out direct hybridization experiments with nuclear and mitochondrial DNA and RNA (cf. the experiments of Dubuy and Riley described above). They concluded that there were certain regions in mitochondrial RNA that were complimentary to nuclear DNA. This would indicate a partial nuclear origin of mitochondrial RNA. There were also some regions that were probably complimentary to MDNA, although the results were not as conclusive. Genetic work with drug-sensitive strains of yeast (see Chapter Eight) also indicates that the synthesis of mitochondrial ribosomes may be under nuclear control. There are now many clear and promising lines for future work, and there is little doubt that elucidation of the function of mitochondrial RNA will result in a great advance in our understanding of the mechanism of mitochondrial biogenesis.

CHAPTER TWO

Labelling of Mitochondria *in vivo*

Labelling experiments *in vivo* are perhaps the nearest the biologist can come to obtaining information about the cell without disturbing it. However, the principle of uncertainty sees to it that the results of such experiments are very rarely unequivocal, and are usually open to many alternative explanations. Perhaps the greatest unknown element is the nature of the 'pool' in the living cell. A rigorous interpretation of labelling experiments would have to include data on the size and rate of labelling of the pool. Such information is often difficult to obtain.

Given these reservations, let us discuss experiments that have been carried out with labelling *in vivo*.

Labelling experiments with animal cells

We will be mainly concerned with labelling of mitochondrial proteins. Although there has been great emphasis on the microsomal fraction in most studies on protein synthesis, it is by no means the case in all tissues that the microsomal fraction is the most rapidly labelled *in vivo*. In particular, many plant tissues show comparable rates of labelling of the mitochondrial and microsomal fractions (see, e.g., Parthier, 1963). An example of this which was established some time ago in the rate of labelling of muscle mitochondria, which is entirely comparable to that of the microsomal system (McClean, Cohn, Brandt, and Simpson, 1958). A probable explanation for the high initial rate of labelling of the mammalian-liver microsome fraction is that the liver is the main site of synthesis in the mammal of serum albumin. A great deal of the rapid labelling observed in liver is, in fact, due to the synthesis of serum albumin. In tissues where there is a great deal of synthesis of protein 'for export' (e.g. in a secretory process) the rough endoplasmic reticulum is very well developed, and high rates of labelling of the microsomal fraction are observed. Thus liver may in fact be a special and not necessarily typical case for examination of labelling *in vivo*.

In recent years there have been some interesting and detailed studies of the labelling of mitochondria *in vivo*. Perhaps the first study specifically directed at examining questions of mitochondrial biogenesis is that of Fletcher and Sanadi (1961). Rats were injected with ^{35}S-

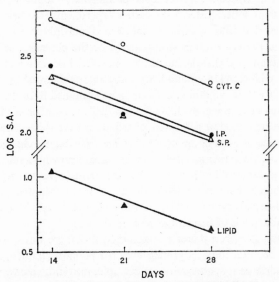

FIG. 4 Logarithmic decay of label in mitochondrial components
Rat-liver mitochondria were labelled *in vivo* and the radioactivity followed in cytochrome *c*, insoluble protein (I.P.). soluble protein (S.P.), and lipid. Note that the half-life for the decay of all four constituents is identical
(From Fletcher and Sanadi, 1961, with kind permission of the authors)

methionine or ^{14}C-acetate and the radioactivity examined in mitochondrial lipid, soluble protein, insoluble protein, and cytochrome *c*. Instead of determining the initial rates of labelling of these components, Fletcher and Sanadi followed the decay in radioactivity over a period of many days (Fig. 4). In this way they were able to determine the *half-life* for decay of the various mitochondrial constituents. Although there was some variability in the results obtained in the first few days, thereafter it appeared quite clearly that the half-life for all the components studied were very similar indeed, and was calculated at 10·3 days. It was concluded from these studies that mitochondria are labile structures and that 'they are turning over as an entity'. In a recent study, Bailey, Taylor, and Bartley (1967) found that the insoluble proteins of rat-liver mitochondria had a half-life of nine days, in good agreement with Fletcher and Sanadi. The turnover of lipids was found to be more complex than appeared from the earlier experiments (see below).

The view that mitochondria are not formed suddenly at one particular moment in the cell cycle is strengthened by the observations of Droz and Bergeron (1965). ^{3}H-leucine was injected into rats and the appearance of label in kidney and liver mitochondria followed by electron-microscope autoradiography. Sections were examined from ten minutes to six hours after injection. It was found that the number of grains per mitochondrion showed a Poisson distribution over this entire period. Also the total number of grains *per mitochondrion* did not change greatly in this time. (Injection of labelled amino acids into whole animals is in effect a 'pulse-labelling' experiment, since after a very sharp rise in specific radioactivity in the plasma in the first few minutes, the radioactivity then falls rather rapidly, as the amino acids are diluted by the considerable pools of free amino acids in the animal.)

Droz and Bergeron therefore concluded that there was a *continuous* synthesis of mitochondrial protein over the period examined. Had the mitochondria been synthesized, for example, just at the moment of cell division, one would have expected mitochondria made after the original 'pulse' to be virtually non-radioactive. The result would have been a skew distribution in the frequency of grains per mitochondrion. Droz and Bergeron point out that if the half-life of the mitochondrion in rat kidney or liver is ten to twelve days, one would only expect $\frac{1}{350}$ to $\frac{1}{400}$ of the mitochondrion to be renewed every hour.

We will discuss Luck's related experiments with *Neurospora crassa* later. We may now mention further work on the labelling of animal cells *in vivo* which is relevant to the problem. An important question is whether the proteins in the various sub-mitochondrial fractions are labelled at the same rate *in vivo*. Truman (1963) sub-fractionated rat-liver mitochondria at various times after the injection of radioactive amino acids. He found that, in general, the relatively insoluble proteins associated with the membrane of the mitochondrion were more radioactive than the bulk of the soluble proteins. This finding complemented observations at the time with labelling *in vitro* (see Chapter Three). The differences in specific radioactivity were not very great, however, and there was some variability in the results. A more detailed kinetic study of the problem has recently been made by Beattie, Basford, and Koritz (1966). They examined the rates of labelling *in vivo* of total soluble proteins, cytochrome *c*, structural protein, and a myosin-like insoluble protein. Using rat-liver and rat-kidney mitochondria, they found that the higher specific radioactivity in the soluble protein observed by Truman (1963) only occurred for relatively short labelling times (e.g. 2–5 minutes). At later times the soluble proteins became progressively more radioactive, particularly with kidney mitochondria. Finally, after eight hours *all the proteins attained the same specific radioactivity*. A plot of the kinetics of labelling *in vivo* observed by Beattie *et al.* is shown in Fig. 5. As mentioned above, Fletcher and Sanadi had found that the rate of decay of soluble and insoluble mitochondrial protein appeared to be identical. Since these proteins had reached the same radioactivity after eight hours, it is possible that we have to distinguish carefully between the mechanism of mitochondrial formation and that of mitochondrial breakdown. The two processes may well be very different. Thus in many cells mitochondria may be degraded by the action of lysosome-like structures (Novikoff and Essner, 1962).

Beattie and co-workers concluded that structural proteins (and possibly other membrane-bound proteins) are made *in situ* in the mitochondrion, but the soluble proteins (including cytochrome *c*) are made elsewhere and in some way incorporated into the mitochondrial structure. This view is fully consistent with the results of labelling of mitochondrial protein *in vitro* (see Chapter Three). There is, indeed, a growing body of evidence that certain mitochondrial soluble proteins, and in particular cytochrome *c*, are made by non-mitochondrial ribosomes. Haldar *et al.* (1966) exposed ascites cells to mild osmotic shock which was sufficient to increase the permeability of the cells to exogenous proteins, but did not seriously affect their viability. The cells were then incubated with suitable concentration of ribonuclease for five minutes. The enzyme permeated the cells, and most of the cytoplasmic ribosomes were destroyed, but the mitochondria appeared to remain

C

more or less intact. When these cells were incubated with radioactive amino acids, there was significant inhibition of incorporation into microsomal proteins and cytochrome c. However, the labelling of the total mitochondrial protein was not seriously affected. It was concluded that cytochrome c is synthesized on extra-mitochondrial cytoplasmic ribosomes.

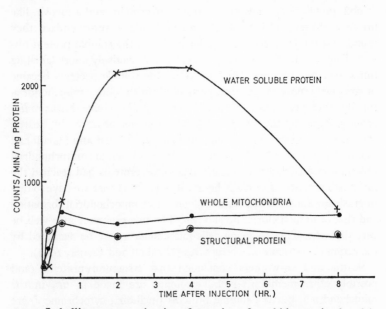

FIG. 5 Labelling patterns *in vivo* of proteins of rat-kidney mitochondria (Plotted from data in Beattie *et al.*, 1966)

Gonzáles-Cadavid and Campbell (1967) have recently made some very interesting observations on the site of synthesis of cytochrome c. Rats were injected with ^{14}C-lysine and at various intervals the livers were sub-fractionated into the classical nuclear, mitochondrial, microsomal, and soluble fractions. Cytochrome c was isolated from all fractions and it was quite striking that the most radioactive cytochrome c *first appeared in the microsomal fraction*. These authors concluded that the protein was first synthesized in the endoplasmic reticulum and incorporated into a membrane fragment ('microsomal particle'). It was subsequently assembled into the mitochondrion.

These studies of labelling of animal cells *in vivo* therefore suggest quite strongly that the soluble mitochondrial proteins have a different site of synthesis from the insoluble membrane-bound proteins. We have the picture of part of the mitochondrion being assembled in the endoplasmic reticulum region of the cell, and another part being made *in situ*. It is important to distinguish two processes in these studies: (i) the synthesis of a *new* mitochondrion and (ii) the growth of a pre-formed mitochondrion. The matter is discussed more fully in Chapter Five, but at this point we should emphasize that it is by no means certain that new mitochondria are formed entirely by growth and division of components in old mitochondria. Non-mitochondrial components are clearly introduced at some point in the process of mitochondrial formation.

Experiments with micro-organisms
We may now describe the excellent experiments of Luck with mitochondria from *Neurospora crassa* (Luck, 1963, 1965). A choline-requiring mutant was used which when grown in the presence of radioactive choline gave highly labelled mitochondrial phospholipids. The labelled cells were then transferred to a non-radioactive medium and allowed to grow through three more cell cycles. The cells were then disrupted, the mitochondria isolated, and examined by autoradiography. It was found that the numbers of grains per mitochondrion were distributed in a random, Poisson distribution, both in mitochondria from freshly labelled cells, and from cells grown in the non-radioactive medium. The experiment is similar to that of Droz and Bergeron (1965) described above, but by using a rapidly growing organism, Luck was able to make a more rigorous analysis of the results. The key observation is that there is no skewness in the labelling pattern after growth in non-radioactive medium. Thus 'young' mitochondria are not completely unlabelled, as would be expected if they had been synthesized 'de novo' from (unlabelled) non-mitochondrial precursors.

Luck concluded from his experiments that there is no 'sudden' assembly of the mitochondrion at one point in time in the cell cycle. Rather mitochondria grow steadily during the cycle by addition of new substance to old. Luck's experiments are sometimes put forward as conclusive proof that mitochondria arise by 'growth and division'. This is perhaps a rather extreme interpretation of his findings, particularly since the experiments only followed the behaviour of mitochondrial lipids. Indeed, his precise conclusion was: 'The data suggest that the mitochondrial mass is increased by a continuous process of addition of new lecithin units to the already existing mitochondrial framework.' Luck (1963) stated that it was unlikely that there had been exchange and redistribution within a pool of radioactive lipids during his experiments. Rearrangement and relocation of subcellular lipid components during cell growth could certainly confuse the result, since it may well result in some labelling of newly formed mitochondria.

In a later study of this system, Luck (1965) made the interesting observation that in the choline-requiring mutant of *Neurospora crassa* which he used, the ratio of phospholipid to protein in mitochondria could be varied considerably by altering the amount of choline in the medium. The amounts of respiratory enzymes per mg protein were not affected, and it appears as if the rates of synthesis of phospholipids and proteins are not closely inter-related. It is therefore clear that it may well be dangerous to draw conclusions about the synthesis of mitochondrial proteins from experiments with lipid precursors. Luck's observations raise the important question of the mechanism of integration of lipids into the growing mitochondrion. There is evidence that mitochondria are able to synthesize certain lipids (these findings are summarized in Roodyn, 1967), but it is far from clear at the moment whether the mitochondrion is 'self-sufficient' as regards its lipids, or whether cytoplasmic lipids are used during mitochondrial formation. In a study of the turnover of membrane lipids in brain mitochondria, Cuzner, Davison, and Gregson (1966) found that cholesterol, cardiolipin, and phosphatidic acid turned over slowly, if at all, whereas the remaining phosphatides had much shorter half-lives. They suggested that the first group of lipids corresponded to more essential 'structural' lipids, whereas the phosphatides are more non-structural and exchange readily with cytoplasmic phospholipids. All this is to emphasize that when considering the results on the 'turnover' of mitochondria we have to be very careful to specify which component has been examined.

Yeast provides an excellent experimental tool for the study of mitochondrial biogenesis (see Chapters Five and Six). Jayaraman, Cotman,

Mahler, and Sharp (1966) have recently carried out an interesting study of labelling of mitochondria *in vivo*. *Saccharomyces cerevisiae*, when grown in the presence of glucose, has poorly defined mitochondria, low respiratory activity, and obtains its energy mainly by fermentation. (There have been many detailed studies of the biochemistry of this 'glucose repression' – see Chapters Five and Six; also Polakis, Bartley, and Meek, 1965.) If the cells are then transferred to a medium containing another carbon source (such as ethanol, lactate, glycerol, or even another carbohydrate such as sucrose), the glucose repression is relieved ('glucose de-repression') and the synthesis of active functional mitochondria takes place. Jayaraman and co-workers incubated yeast with radioactive amino acids during this process of de-repression and then followed the radioactivity in mitochondria and various sub-mitochondrial fragments. They also made extensive enzymic analyses on the fractions, and followed the changes by electron microscopy. Their conclusions are perhaps best given by direct quotation from their papers (p. 248): '. . . the average cell in the fully repressed population is characterized by a small number of the mitochondria, plus a large proportion of particulates, probably membranous structures, or "promitochondria". In the de-repressed phase these promitochondria then are reorganized and converted into functional mitochondria by the acquisition of additional structural and functional components. . . .'

Recently there has been some interesting research done into the biosynthesis and genetics of yeast cytochrome *c* that may well be of general significance. As discussed in Chapter Six, it is now well established that the amino-acid sequence of yeast cytochrome *c* is controlled by a chromosomal gene. Mattoon and Sherman (1966) exploited this to make some interesting studies on the binding of cytochrome *c* to mitochondria. They isolated mitochondria from a mutant that could not produce cytochrome *c*. These mitochondria showed a greatly diminished oxygen uptake, and had low P/O ratios for succinate oxidation. If cytochrome *c* was added to the deficient mitochondria, there was full restoration of normal respiratory and phosphorylative activity. The added cytochrome *c* became tightly bound to the mitochondria and remained attached even after re-isolation. It has been known for many years that there is a loose association between cytochrome *c* and the respiratory system, and that cytochrome *c* can be *reversibly* removed without permanent damage to the oxidative phosphorylation system. The observations of Mattoon and Sherman therefore indicate that the specific insertion of proteins made on non-mitochondrial ribosomes into an organized mitochondrial membrane is by no means impossible. They suggest, in fact, that the phenomenon they have observed *in vitro* may occur *in vivo*, i.e. that 'cytochrome *c* is synthesized in the cytoplasm and is spontaneously incorporated into the mitochondria at a specific functional site'.

It is clear, therefore, that there is very strong evidence from experiments *in vivo* that most soluble mitochondrial proteins in general and cytochrome *c* in particular are made in non-mitochondrial sites, and subsequently incorporated into the mitochondrial structure. The genetic control and precise mechanism of synthesis of mitochondrial soluble protein is still not fully understood, but the system for which we have the most information, namely yeast cytochrome *c*, is undoubtedly complex (Fukuhara and Sels, 1966). It is likely that the next few years will reveal the fine details of sensitive control mechanisms that we require to integrate soluble protein with an organized membrane structure.

It also appears from most of the studies with labelling *in vivo* that there is no sudden increase in the rate of mitochondrial constituents during the cell cycle. In confirmation of this, Kahn and Blum (1967) have recently studied the labelling of mitochondrial proteins in *Astasia longa*. They found that the ratio of the rate of mitochondrial protein synthesis to that of total cellular proteins remained constant throughout the cell cycle. There thus seems little doubt that the elaboration of the mitochondrial population occurs steadily during the growth of the cell.

CHAPTER THREE

Mitochondrial Protein Synthesis

General characteristics of the amino-acid incorporation system

A diagrammatic summary of the main properties of the mitochondrial incorporation system is given in Roodyn (1966a). Mitochondrial fractions from a wide range of biological material have been shown to incorporate radioactive amino acids into protein on incubation *in vitro*. These include mitochondrial fractions from micro-organisms, plants, invetebrate and vertebrate animals. Not all these fractions have been examined with equal care or interest, and we must be cautious not to generalize, for example, from rat liver to *Tetrahymena pyriformis*. Nevertheless, there are strong indications that most of the incorporation systems have similar properties.

One of the most striking properties of the incorporation system is the relative simplicity of the media used to demonstrate activity. Since there is no obvious requirement for added cell sap, or pH 5 enzyme, mitochondria incubated, for example, in a medium containing buffer, Mg^{2+} ions, adenine nucleotides, an amino-acid mixture, and an energy source (e.g. succinate) show adequate incorporation (Roodyn *el al.*, 1961). There is still some confusion as to whether addition of an oxidizable substrate is required (see below), and the precise requirements for amino acids is also unclear. Some workers therefore simply use media that maintain mitochondrial oxidative phosphorylation, without adding substrates or amino acids. It is fair to say at the moment that there is still a great deal to be done before an 'optimum' assay system is developed. As will be made clear shortly, there is now little doubt that the final amino-acid incorporation observed is affected by a number of complex and interacting factors which will require subtle methods to control.

The incorporation usually proceeds for about 90–120 minutes and then the rate falls off, often to zero. Incorporation levels in counts/mg protein (or better $\mu\mu$moles/mg protein) are rather low. However, even well-washed mitochondria contain a considerable pool of free amino acids (Truman and Korner, 1962), which is difficult to saturate (Roodyn et al., 1961; Roodyn, 1965). Also the amount of RNA per mg protein is low (10–20 μg). When the effect of dilution by endogenous pool is taken into account, the rate of incorporation is comparable to a good microsomal system, if the results are expressed on an RNA, rather than on a protein, basis. The incorporation is dependent on mitochondrial oxidation phosphorylation and is inhibited by anaerobiosis, cyanide, and 2:4 dinitrophenol. At least in the case of rat liver, it is also dependent on the continuous supply of endogenous ATP, since incubation of well-washed mitochondria for short times (fifteen to thirty minutes) in the absence of oxidizable substrate leads to irreversible inhibition (Roodyn et al., 1961, Roodyn, 1965). The incorporation also appears to be dependent on the maintenance of mitochondrial structure, since it is inhibited by isolation in hypotonic media, excessive mechanical damage, or lysis by detergents (see, e.g., Roodyn, 1965). The major radioactive product appears to be insoluble protein associated with the membrane, and probably related to structural protein (S.P.). The incorporation is probably dependent, at least partially, on the continual synthesis of RNA by a DNA-dependent RNA polymerase (Kroon, 1965). It has not yet been shown unequivocally that mitochondrial ribosomes are the site of the activity, but there is now a great deal of strongly suggestive evidence that this is indeed so.

The incorporation is resistant to quite high concentrations of RNase, but is sensitive to chloramphenicol. These properties distinguish it most markedly from isolated microsomal systems. The incorporation observed in vitro appears to reflect physiological and hormonal changes in vivo.

Some of these characteristics of the systems will now be discussed in more detail.

Non-mitochondrial contaminants, especially bacteria
There is little doubt that the incorporation is not due to microsomal contamination. It has been a general finding that the system is resistant to the action of added ribonuclease (e.g. McLean et al., 1958; Kroon,

1963a). Kroon (1964) exploited this fact in the preparation of mito-chondria for his incorporation experiments by regularly pre-incubating with ribonuclease. Washing experiments have indicated that the residual microsomal contamination cannot account for the observed activity (McLean et al., 1958; Roodyn et al., 1961). There is no correlation between glucose-6-phosphatase activity and radioactive protein when labelled mitochondria are analysed on sucrose gradients (Roodyn, Free-man, and Tata, 1965). As discussed in greater detail below, chloram-phenicol inhibits the mitochondrial, but not the microsomal system. There is no requirement for pH enzymes or cell sap (e.g. Roodyn et al., 1961). The mitochondrial system is resistant to quite high concentra-tions of EDTA, which would inactivate cytoplasmic ribosomes, and incorporates poorly when incubated in a 'microsomal' medium. Con-versely microsomal fractions are inactive in the 'mitochondrial' medium (Roodyn et al., 1965).

There is not such conclusive evidence that lysosomes do not contri-bute. However, the authors are not aware of any reports of amino-acid incorporation by purified preparation of lysosomes, and there is no correlation between radioactivity and acid phosphatase on sucrose gradients (Roodyn et al., 1965). The problem of bacterial contamina-tion is important. The reader may have been aware, by now, that in many of its properties the mitochondrial incorporation system re-sembles that of free bacteria. The media required are relatively simple: a specific antibiotic, chloramphenicol, inhibits the system but does not affect microsomal incorporation; ribonuclease and EDTA have no effect. Bacteria are very difficult to separate from mitochondria, and indeed would be expected to be concentrated in the mitochondrial fraction. The arguments against bacterial contamination are as follows: The incorporation observed shows no relationship to the number of bacteria present. Some authors report dependence on the presence of an oxidizable substrate, even in a complex medium containing many possible carbon sources (including glucose) that could be used by bacteria. Simple omission of succinate from such a complex medium results in irreversible inhibition after thirty minutes (Roodyn, 1965). The progress curves in the first two hours of incubation show no similarity to progress curves observed with bacteria. Also, requirements for Mg^{2+} ions, P_i, and adenine nucleotides are difficult to explain if the effect is due to bacteria. Although there was not complete separation of bacteria and radioactive protein on a sucrose gradient, there was no obvious correlation (Roodyn et al., 1965). Complete separation between bacteria and labelled mitochondria has recently been reported by Simpson, Fournier, and Skinner (1967). The behaviour of the system in response to physiological changes in the whole animal is difficult to explain in terms of bacterial contamination. For example, the amino-acid incorporation system in brain mitochondria appears to respond to drugs that affect nervous activity (Campbell, Mahler, Moore, and Tewari, 1966). Indeed, in experiments in which the incorporation was enhanced by administration of thyroid hormones to the whole animal there was no correlation at all with the measured bacterial count (Roodyn et al., 1965). There have been numerous reports of resistance of the system to certain antibiotics (e.g. penicillin plus streptomycin (Kalf, 1963) or penicillin plus a range of antibiotics including ristomycin, vanomycin, and novobiocin (Haldar et al., 1967)), and there have been many other arguments of an indirect nature which argue against bacterial contamination (Roodyn, 1966b; Kroon, 1966a).

Recently experiments with mitochondrial preparations essentially free of bacteria have confirmed that the incorporation system is still active. Lado and Schwendimann (1967) isolated mitochondria from plants under sterile conditions, and obtain significant incorporation, although the preparation was far less active than that contaminated with bacteria. Yellin, Butler, and Stein (1967) have described a typical amino-acid incorporation system in a mitochondrial fraction isolated from rat brain under sterile conditions. Wheeldon (1966), by indirect experiments, ascribed the RNase-resistant incorporation to bacteria, although he stated that the bulk of the incorporation was mitochondrial. Kroon, Saccone, and Botman (1967) have questioned this view. Using sterile media and instruments, they obtained preparations of liver mitochondria that contained no viable bacteria. They incorporated ^{14}C-leucine into protein at precisely the same rate as non-sterile mitochondria, and the incorporation was *not* inhibited by ribonuclease. Thus it appears that the ribonuclease resistance is a true property of the mitochondria. Grivell (1967) has isolated mitochondria from protoplasts of *Saccharomyces carlsbergensis* under germ-free conditions, and obtained an active system free of bacteria and whole yeast cells. Nevertheless, it shows the usual resistance to ribonuclease and sensitivity to chloramphenicol. There have been other reports of the isolation of essentially bacteria-free mitochondria that still incorporate in the usual way (Beattie, Basford and Koritz, 1967; Simpson, Fournier, and Skinner, 1967; Work, 1967). Also, activating enzymes and tRNA's have been demonstrated in mitochondria from *Neurospora crassa* isolated under virtually germ-free conditions (Barnett *et al.*, 1967). (Davies and Cocking, 1967, have recently demonstrated amino-acid incorporation by germ-free preparations of plastids from tomato tissue. The preparation had many similar properties to the mitochondrial system.)

Sandell, Löw, and der Decken (1967) have recently observed, however, that rat-liver mitochondria isolated under germ-free conditions appear to be inactive. It is not clear at the moment why they have obtained inactive preparations, while other workers have obtained fully active mitochondria in the absence of bacteria. The methods used for isolation and incubation by Sandell and co-workers differ somewhat from the techniques of other workers, and they have not demonstrated that mitochondria isolated by a variety of techniques are all inactive. In view of the complexity of the incorporation system, and its sensitivity to a wide range of agents, it is probably unwise to place too much reliance on negative findings. Certainly, the balance of evidence at the present time is strongly against bacteria being the cause of the incorporation, provided that the mitochondrial preparation is reasonably intact and the number of bacteria present is not much greater than 10^5 per ml.

Relation to mitrochondrial metabolism, especially amino-acid metabolism and oxidative phosphorylation

There is no doubt that the incorporation process is intimately connected with many aspects of mitochondrial metabolism. Considering the amino acids first, we have mentioned above that isolated mitochondria still retain a considerable pool of free amino acids. We know remarkably little about the composition of this pool, and its behaviour in different states. However, it is quite clear the amino-acid pool will have a profound effect on the final level of amino-acid incorporation observed.

Early studies indicated that mitochondria contain amino-acid-activating enzymes. Thus Reis, Coote, and Work (1959) reported amino-acid-dependent ATP–pyrophosphate exchange. Activating enzymes for several amino acids were also reported by Craddock and Simpson (1961). Truman and Korner (1962) also showed that a soluble extract of mitochondria could replace cell sap in a ribosomal system. Recently Barnett *et al.* (1967) have demonstrated the presence of a family of amino-acid-activating enzymes in mitochondria isolated from *Neurospora crassa* Three of the enzymes, the aspartic acid, leucine, and phenylalanine-activating enzymes clearly differ from the corresponding non-mitochondrial enzymes.

Some of the amino acids (particularly glutamate) can act as energy sources for the incorporation process (Roodyn, 1965). This confuses the interpretation of studies on the effect of added amino acids on incorporation. Most workers usually add a mixture of amino acids, perhaps more out of good faith than conviction, and no one has yet tackled the daunting task of systematically studying the effect of various combinations of all the amino acids. Wheeldon and Lehninger (1966) came to the conclusion that only proline and arginine stimulated ^{14}C-leucine incorporation. They also observed that there was a rapid uptake of radioactive leucine into the intra-mitochondrial pool in the first few minutes of incubation (Fig. 6). This uptake was energy-linked, and possibly due to a specific transport mechanism (cf. Garfinkel, 1963). Surprisingly, we are really very ignorant about the mechanism of transport of amino acids across the membrane system. We can perhaps summarize by saying that the concentrations of free, activated, and SRNA-bound amino acids are the result of complex structural and metabolic interactions. Some aspects of these complexities are discussed in Roodyn (1965).

Unfortunately we have similar difficulties when we come to consider the relationship of the incorporation process to oxidative metabolism and oxidative phosphorylation. There is some confusion as to whether there is a requirement for an *added* oxidizable substrate. Some workers find that the mitochondria (or sub-mitochondrial fractions) incorporate quite happily in the absence of any added substrate (e.g. Kroon, 1965; Truman and Löw, 1963). In fact, addition of succinate, for example, actually results in apparent *inhibition* of incorporation. Other workers, however (e.g. McLean *et al.*, 1958; Roodyn *et al.*, 1961; Kalf, 1963), have observed considerable stimulation on adding substrates. In a detailed study of this question it was shown (Roodyn, 1965) that a range of oxidizable substrates was effective, the actual stimulation obtained depending markedly on the concentration of substrate. It is still unclear why such differences in behaviour should be observed. There are many differences in technique by the various workers, and it may be that preservation or loss of the intra-mitochondrial pool of substrates during isolations may affect the results. Certainly some remarkable changes in composition of the pool of endogenous substrates can occur with time (Olson and von Korff, 1967). Once again the problem of the endogenous

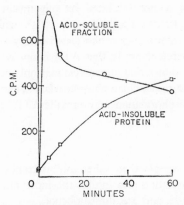

FIG. 6 Uptake of ^{14}C-leucine into acid-soluble and acid-insoluble fractions

Rat-liver mitochondria were incubated with radioactive amino acid and extracted with 5 per cent trichloroacetic acid

(From Wheeldon and Lehninger, 1966, by kind permission of the authors)

pool of metabolites arises, and we will probably not understand the finer detailes of mitochondrial protein synthesis until more is known about this subject. It is has also become clear recently that the uptake of many oxidizable substrates is not by passive diffusion but by a controlled process that is affected by the state of the mitochondrial membrane.

The precise source of energy for the incorporation process is still not known. There is little doubt that the systems in the mitochondria for oxidative phosphorylation and protein synthesis are located in physical proximity, i.e. in the mitochondrial membrane. Thus energy-rich inter-mediates other than ATP (i.e. the so called 'non-phosphorylated energy-rich' or '∽' compounds) may act as an energy source. However, this is rather difficult to establish conclusively. Wheeldon and Lehniger (1966) reported that they obtained the best incorporation with an external ATP generating source (phosphoenol-pyruvate plus pyruvate kinase). However, other workers have found that extra mitochondrial ATP is not as effective as ADP or AMP, and rely on mitochondrial energy production to produce ATP (McLean *et al.*, 1958; Kalf, 1963). The incorporation is not inhibited by oligomycin (Wheeldon and Lehninger, 1966; Bronk, 1963; Kroon, 1964), which prevents the formation of ATP from non-phosphorylated energy-rich intermediates, and this would therefore imply that ATP is not required. However, Kroon (1966b) has shown that oligomycin may only be preventing ATP formation from respiratory chain phosphorylation, and it is possible that substrate-level phosphorylation may provide ATP for the amino-acid incorporation.

Effect of inhibitors

A wide variety of agents that either inhibit respiration or uncouple oxidation phosphorylation also inhibit the incorporation process (e.g. anaerobiosis, cyanide, and 2:4 dinitrophenol).

Experiments with inhibitors of protein synthesis are of greater interest. First of all, partial or complete inhibition with *puromycin* has been reported by several workers (e.g. Kroon, 1963b, 1965). Puromycin prevents the formation of complete peptide chains from amino acyl–SRNA, and with ribosomal systems incomplete chains with puromycin attached are released (see, e.g., Nathans, 1964). The inhibition of the mitochondrial system by this agent is therefore a good indication that true peptide formation is occurring.

There have been some most interesting studies with the inhibitor *Actinomycin D*. This is a cytostatic agent. It appears to act as a specific inhibitor of DNA-dependent RNA polymerase. DNA-dependent RNA polymerase has been reported in mitochondria, and like other RNA polymerases is sensitive to actinomycin D. Kroon (1963b) observed incomplete inhibition of amino-acid incorporation in mitochondria, and concluded that mitochondrial DNA is functionally active in mitochondrial amino-acid incorporation. He suggested that the linearity he observed in the incorporation system over a period of hours may be due to the continual production of messenger RNA within the mitochondrion. The question of permeability is important, since Wheeldon and Lehninger (1966) did not observe inhibition if they used intact mitochondria, but could observe it in digitonin or sonic fragments. It thus seems quite likely that mitochondrial DNA controls the amino-acid incorporation system via the synthesis of RNA in the mitochondrion.

Recently there have been most important findings with the inhibitor *chloramphenicol* (see Chapter Eight). The sensitivity of the mitochondrial system to chloramphenicol is one of the most important respects in which it differs from the microsomal system. Inhibition of incorporation has been reported in a wide range of mitochondrial fractions (e.g. Kroon, 1965; Mager, 1960; Wheeldon and Lehninger, 1966). The drug does not inhibit incorporation of amino acids *in vitro* with cytoplasmic ribosomes in animals (e.g. from rabbit reticulocytes: Von Ehrenstein and Lipmann, 1961), and, more important from the theoretical interpretation of some current work, *yeast* cytoplasmic ribosomes are equally insensitive (Bretthauer, Marcus, Chaloupka, Halvorson, and Bock, 1963). Incorporation *in vitro* with yeast mitochondria, however, is inhibited by the drug (Wintersberger, 1965). It is also most interesting that ribosomes from chloroplasts are sensitive to chloramphenicol (Eisenstadt and Brawerman, 1964). There is thus an interesting connexion between bacterial systems (which are sensitive to the drug) and mitochondrial and chloroplast (plastid) systems (see Chapter Four).

The action of inhibitors has been discussed recently by Borst *et al.* 1967), and they have conveniently summarized these effects in a table (Table 1). (It may be noted in the table that cycloheximide does not inhibit mitochondrial incorporation, but acriflavin does (see Chapters Six and Eight). Also, on the basis of evidence given in Chapter One we might insert a value of 55–60 S for the $S_{20, w}$ of mitochondrial ribosomes.)

Site of amino-acid incorporation

It has been observed generally that the bulk of the amino-acid incorporation observed with isolated mitochondria is into insoluble protein. In

order to define the site of incorporation more precisely, rat-liver mitochondria labelled *in vitro* with ^{14}C-valine were disrupted by treatment
with the neutral detergent, Triton-X-100, and sub-fractionated by
differential centrifuging (Roodyn, 1962). Negligible radioactivity was
found in the soluble fraction. The most radioactive protein was in a
fraction sedimenting after one hour at 100,000 g, and rich in RNA,

TABLE I　Protein synthesis: properties in different systems

	Micro-somal systems	Mito-chondria (intact)	Chloro-plasts	Bacteria
Inhibition by:				
Actinomycin D	−	±	±	+
Acriflavin (2 µg/ml)	−	++		−
Chloramphenicol	−	++	+	++
Puromycin	++	+	++	++
Cycloheximide	++	−		−
Deoxyribonuclease	−	−	±	−
Ribonuclease	++	−	++	−
Dinitrophenol (5 × 10^{-5}M)	−	++		+
Swelling		+	+	−
Requirement for:				
pH 5 enzymes	++	−	−?	−
External ATP	++	−	++	−
$S_{20,w}$ value ribosomes	80		70	70

(Table from Borst *et al.*, 1967, with kind permission of the authors)

phospholipid, and succinoxidase. This without doubt corresponded to
membrane fractions isolated by similar techniques by other workers.
(The incorporation into the various sub-mitochondrial fractions is
shown in Fig. 7.) These results suggested strongly that the mitochondrial membrane was the major site of incorporation. Studies by
Truman and Korner (1962), and Kroon (1965) confirmed this by showing that preparations of mitochondrial membranes could incorporate
radioactive amino acids *in vitro*.

Wheeldon and Lehninger (1966) have recently obtained very similar
results to those of Roodyn (1962). Rat-liver mitochondria were labelled

in vitro with ^{14}C-leucine and disrupted by ultrasonic vitrations. Sub-fractionation showed that there was negligible incorporation into the soluble fraction. The most radioactive protein was found in 'light fragments' of the mitochondrial membrane. The bulk of the radioactive protein in the membrane was structural protein (S.P.) (see below).

Recently Neupert, Brdiczka, and Bücher (1967) have made the following most interesting findings. Rat-liver mitochondria were labelled *in vitro* with ^{14}C-leucine and the inner and outer membranes separated

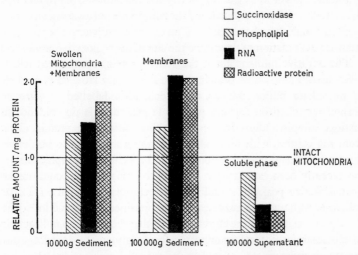

FIG. 7 Sub-fractionation of mitochondria labelled *in vitro* with ^{14}C-valine (Data from Roodyn *et al.*, 1961)

by a 'swelling–shrinking' method. By use of appropriate enzyme markers it was calculated that the outer membrane had a specific radio-activity less than 5 per cent of that of the inner membrane, and it was concluded that amino-acid incorporation *in vitro* occurs only into the inner membrane. It thus now appears to be quite firmly established that the mitochondrial membrane is the site of amino-acid incorporation, and that it is the inner membrane which is active. Neupert and co-workers discuss in this paper some very recent evidence indicating that the inner and outer mitochondrial membranes are synthesized by different systems *in vivo*.

D

The radioactive product

The energy-dependence of the incorporation and its sensitivity to puromycin strongly suggest that the incorporation is due to the formation of labelled peptides, and not to an artifactual adsorption of radioactive amino acids on to protein. Several workers have shown by treatment with fluorodinitrobenzene and other reagents that the incorporation is into the interior of the peptide chain (e.g. Roodyn *et al.*, 1961). Thus there are strong indications that the incorporation is indeed due to protein synthesis. However, as we will shortly see, the radioactive product is, at the moment, rather ill-defined, and the authors are not aware of an experiment in which there has been isolation of a pure radioactive peptide, and stepwise degradation to determine the site of the radioactive amino acid.

The negative findings about the actual proteins synthesized will be given first. The 'soluble protein fraction' is poorly labelled as a whole. If phosphate buffer extracts of mitochondria labelled *in vitro* are chromatographed on calcium phosphate gel, there is no evidence for distinct soluble radioactive proteins. The radioactive protein eluted from the column with high salt concentrations appears to be derived from contaminant insoluble lipoprotein. This chromatographic analysis has recently been extended by Kadenbach (1967a), who could observe no radioactive peaks in soluble extracts chromatographed on TEAE-cellulose. Although the enzymes were not purified, one could infer from their peak positions in the chromatogram that there was no radioactivity in glutamate/oxaloacetate aminotransferase, glutamate dehydrogenase, malate dehydrogenase, adenylate kinase, and nucleosidediphosphate kinase. Roodyn *et al.* (1962) in more direct experiments showed that if the enzymes malate dehydrogenase and cytochrome *c* are purified from mitochondria labelled *in vitro*, the level of radioactivity falls very rapidly as the purification proceeds, and the pure enzymes have no detectable radioactivity. Identical findings with cytochrome *c* have been reported by Simpson, Skinner, and Lucas (1961). The absence of labelling of soluble mitochondrial proteins has been confirmed by a number of other workers (e.g. Bronsert and Neupert, 1966).

What, then, is the nature of the radioactive product? As mentioned above, disruption and sub-fractionation of labelled mitochondria indicated that the bulk of the incorporation was into the membrane. It was shown by Roodyn (1962) that most of the radioactivity was associated with an 'RNA–lipoprotein complex' sedimenting after one hour at 100,000 g. Further treatment of this complex with high concentrations of detergent detached a radioactive lipoprotein fraction free of RNA. The residual RNA–protein fraction was much less radioactive than the crude lipoprotein extract. The extracted protein had somewhat similar properties to the structural protein (S.P.) that had been isolated from beef-heart mitochondria by Criddle, Bock, Green, and Tisdale (1962). If S.P. was isolated from rat-liver mitochondria by the method of Criddle and co-workers, it was indeed found to be radioactive, although not as radioactive as the final extracted protein mentioned above. The fractionation scheme in these experiments is given in Fig. 8, together

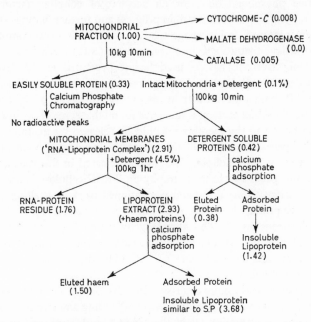

FIG. 8 Fractionation scheme for preparation of radioactive lipoprotein Values in brackets refer to the ratio:

$$\frac{\text{Counts/min/mg protein in fraction}}{\text{Counts/min/mg protein in intact mitochondria}}$$

Mitochondria labelled *in vitro* with ^{14}C-valine
(Data from Roodyn, 1962)

with the specific radioactivities, chemical properties, and possible structural origin of the various fractions.

There is further evidence that S.P. is labelled *in vitro*. Haldar *et al.* (1966) isolated S.P. from labelled mitochondria using the improved isolation method of Richardson, Hultin, and Fleischer (1964). This method gives a preparation of S.P. that is essentially free of contaminants (such as haem, flavin, sialic acid, and lipids). The protein was radioactive. It is interesting that Haldar and co-workers also analysed the radioactive product by electrophoresis on acrylamide gel. Several radioactive bands were observed and one of them had similar migration properties to Racker's coupling factor 4, an intermediate factor in oxidative phosphorylation (for an account of coupling factors see Racker, 1962). This work is still in progress and further findings should be of great interest. It does suggest, however, that it is an oversimplification to believe that a *single* insoluble protein (S.P.) is labelled.

Kadenbach (1967a) has also used the improved method of Richardson *et al.* to isolate S.P. He found that 65 per cent of the total radioactivity was in S.P., with a specific activity about three times that of the original total mitochondrial protein. Kadenbach found that some of the insoluble protein bound to the membrane could be released by treatment with phospholipase. Thus some of the radioactive product is bound to the membrane by phospholipid. The protein released in this way was resolved into peaks by chromatography on TEAE-cellulose. Thus there are indications from all the above mentioned work that, although the radioactive product is similar to S.P. in its properties, it is probably not a homogeneous protein. Our knowledge of the chemistry of proteins of the S.P. type is not yet sufficiently advanced for us to be certain whether or not there are several species of S.P. This question is discussed in greater detail below.

Wheeldon and Lehninger (1966) isolated S.P. from mitochondrial membranes by dissolving in detergent and adding ammonium sulphate to 11 per cent saturation (as in the original method of Criddle *et al.*, 1962). The precipitate was taken as S.P. and the supernatant as 'Other Membrane Protein (O.M.P.)'. After ten minutes labelling of mitochondria *in vitro*, the S.P. was about as radioactive as 'O.M.P.'. However, as the incubation proceeded, S.P. became relatively more radioactive, until it was twice as active as 'O.M.P.'. This could indicate that there is a sequential synthesis of several mitochondrial insoluble membrane proteins, with S.P. being the final product.

These workers also made some interesting observations on the turnover of the labelled product. Wheeldon and Lehninger studied this by prelabelling mitochondria for thirty minutes and then adding 'chaser' ^{12}C-leucine in excess. They found that there was a clear decay in the specific activity of the protein. The decay process was stimulated by addition of puromycin or GTP and was inhibited by antimycin. The decay was probably due to release of 'nascent' polypeptide chains, as has been described by several workers with non-mitochondrial ribosomes.

Thus it appears that the bulk of the incorporation is into insoluble membrane-bound protein, closely related to S.P. It is not yet certain whether one or several species of radioactive insoluble protein are formed, but there are probably several. The radioactive protein(s) appear to be at least partly bound to the membrane by lipid and are in close proximity to the mitochondrial RNA. It is interesting that Gnanam and Kahn (1967) have shown that isolated chloroplasts incorporate radioactive amino acids *in vitro* into structural proteins associated with the membrane. Indeed, the scheme they propose for the mechanism of chloroplast formation shows many similarities to the mitochondrial system (see Fig. 12, p. 52). In particular, they postulate that one of the functions of chloroplast DNA is to encode for structural protein.

Effect of hormonal and physiological changes

Studies on the incorporation system in isolated mitochondria may well give us some indication as to the method of control of mitochondrial protein synthesis *in vivo*. This is because there are many indications that changes that occur in the intact cell affect the activity finally observed *in vitro*. Thus a variety of hormonal changes affect incorporation. It is also affected by drugs given to the whole organism, and is influenced by the age and rate of cell division of the intact cell (e.g. greater activity is observed in new-born rats, or in regenerating rat liver). Details of all these effects will not be discussed here. Instead, as an example, one of the most striking of the hormonal effects will be considered, since it is the best-established case of changes *in vivo*.

It has been known for many years that administration of thyroid hormones results in changes in the levels of many respiratory enzymes. Tata, Ernster, Lindberg, Arrhenius, Pedersen, and Hedman (1963) administered single doses of thyroid hormone to thyroidectomized animals and followed the time sequence of the changes in the levels of various enzymes. The changes they observed were quite striking. It was found that *after a delay of about one and a half days* there is a two- to three-fold increase in a number of mitochondrial enzymes, indicating some sort of reorganization or assembly of mitochondria. At about the

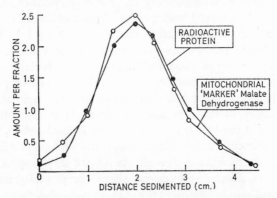

FIG. 9 Co-sedimentation of radioactive protein and mitochondria in sucrose gradient
Mitochondria were labelled *in vitro* with ^{14}C-leucine and malate dehydrogenase used as a marker
(From Roodyn *et al.*, 1965)

same time there was an increase in the level of microsomal enzymes (e.g. glucose-6-phosphatase), and in addition, the amino-acid incorporation activity of the microsomal fraction was greatly enhanced. Tata and co-workers concluded from these findings that thyroid hormone had a general anabolic effect on the cell, and in particular there was enhanced synthesis of mitochondrial respiratory assemblies. The delay of one to two days in the effect showed clearly that the stimulatory action on mitochondrial enzymes and basal metabolic rate was not due to a direct action of thyroid hormones on mitochondria. Thus it was suggested that the well-known enhanced metabolic rate in the hyperthyroid condition was not due to uncoupling of oxidative phosphorylation, as had been generally imagined, but was due to the synthesis of new respiratory proteins.

This view was strongly supported when it was found that at the same time as the stimulation in microsomal incorporation, there was a doubling of the rate of mitochondrial amino-acid incorporation observed *in vitro* (Freeman, Roodyn, and Tata, 1964). This observation was therefore investigated in some detail (Roodyn *et al.*, 1965). It was confirmed that the 'stimulated' particles followed mitochondria very

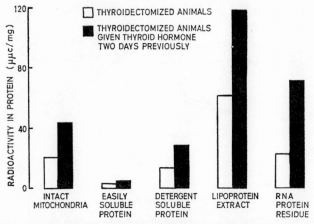

FIG. 10 Labelling patterns of mitochondria *in vitro* from rats with and without thyroid hormone treatment
Mitochondria labelled with ^{14}C-valine and sub-fractionated as in Fig. 7
(Data from Roodyn *et al.*, 1965)

closely in sucrose gradient centrifuging (Fig. 9). It was also shown that the incorporation was not due to bacterial or microsomal contamination. The pattern of labelling in various sub-mitochondrial fractions appeared to be identical in control and stimulated mitochondria (Fig. 10). Although S.P. proteins were not actually isolated, the same general pattern of labelling occurred with and without thyroid stimulation. In the light of the recent studies indicating that cytochrome *c*, and possibly all soluble proteins, are made on cytoplasmic ribosomes (see above), it is interesting that the stimulations of microsomal and mitochondrial amino-acid incorporation occurred at the same time (Fig. 11). This suggests strongly that there is a concerted, integrated synthesis of in-soluble and soluble mitochondrial proteins.

The amount of cytochromes per mg mitochondrial protein increases after the stimulation in amino-acid incorporation, as does the concen-tration of mitochondrial RNA. The reasons for the stimulation *pre-ceding* these changes are not yet clear. It could be that the incorporation system reflects changes in rate of synthesis, but that the net effect of

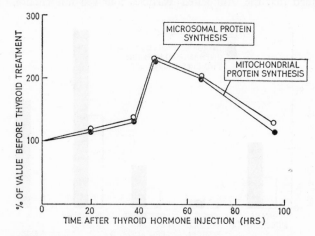

FIG. 11 Stimulation of mitochondrial and microsomal protein synthesis by thyroid hormones

Thyroidectomized rats were injected with tri-iodothyronine, and at various times after, liver mitochondrial and microsomal fractions were incubated *in vitro* with ^{14}C-valine

(from Roodyn *et al.*, 1965)

these changes on total protein takes longer to appear. The mechanism of stimulation is also uncertain, but in view of the finding of Widnell and Tata (1966) that nuclear RNA polymerase is stimulated by thyroid and other hormones, it is possible that a similar mechanism operates with mitochondrial RNA, although the authors are not aware of any direct evidence on this at the moment. The biochemical results which indicate that thyroid hormone stimulates the synthesis of mitochondrial re-spiratory units is fully confirmed by the electron-microscopy findings of Gustaffson, Tata, Lindberg, and Ernster (1965). Greatly elongated mitochondria, with densely packed cristae, were observed in the skeletal muscle of hyperthyroid rats.

It has recently been found by Haldar *et al.* (1966) that repeated injection of thyroid hormone is followed by stimulation of the rate of ^{3}H-thymidine incorporation into MDNA observed *in vitro*. It is thus now quite clear that the major components of the system for mitochondrial biogenesis are profoundly affected by thyroid hormones, and that these changes are reflected by the behaviour of the isolated mitochondria.

Mitochondrial amino-acid incorporation is stimulated in regenerating liver (Braun, Marsh, and Drabkin, 1963). Another interesting example relating changes *in vivo* with changes in the incorporation system is the work of Bronsert and Neupert (1966) with locust mitochondria. Mitochondria were isolated from the flight-muscle of the locust undergoing various stages of development. At the time of imaginal moulting there is a marked increase in the size of the mitochondria (Bücher, 1965). The rate of labelling of protein *in vivo* was greatest immediately after moulting and then fell rapidly. There were complimentary changes observed in the isolated incorporation system.

We can conclude that the incorporation system reflects changes occurring in the whole organism. This gives us greater confidence in the significance of results with isolated mitochondria. It also provides a promising opening for studying factors that affect mitochondrial biogenesis under more controlled conditions than can be obtained with experiments on intact organisms.

Role of insoluble (structural) proteins in mitochondrial formation
In view of the results of the investigations above, something should be said of the properties of mitochondrial structural proteins. The original method of isolation of 'S.P.' (Criddle *et al.*, 1962) is rather simple, involving one ammonium sulphate precipitation of a detergent extract and a few treatments with organic solvents. It may be wondered whether the final product is a pure protein or not. The protein appears to be homogeneous, has a molecular weight between 20,000 and 30,000, and has a characteristic N-acetyl end group, as is found in other insoluble proteins such as myosin (Criddle, Edwards, and Petersen, 1966). However, in view of the simplicity of the isolation method, it is rather surprising that S.P. appears to be a single protein. However, there are great difficulties

in analysing and testing the purity of insoluble proteins and it is possible that improved methods may reveal the existence of several classes of S.P. Since the method of Criddle *et al.* (1962) involves rather drastic treatment with *n*-butanol and 50 per cent methanol, it is probable that most lipoproteins in the original detergent extract would be split, with a possible denaturation of the protein. Denatured protein may well show some of the properties of S.P. (e.g. insolubility in a range of solvents). Thus it is possible that S.P. may contain or even consist of degradation products of other membrane-bound proteins. For example, one wonders what the properties of cytochrome *a* would be after removal of the haem and treatment with organic solvents. It is interesting that S.P. has the ability to bind certain mitochondrial proteins and phospholipids in a specific manner. For example, there appear to be specific binding sites for the important cytochromes of the respiratory chain. As a result, it has been proposed that S.P. is responsible for the correct integration of bound mitochondrial components into the organized membrane (Criddle *et al.*, 1962). Mitochondrial DNA may thus encode for the synthesis of S.P. (or a family of insoluble molecules of similar properties). Most, or all, of the specific mitochondrial components may be synthesized elsewhere (e.g. on cytoplasmic ribosomes), and assembled by interaction with these insoluble proteins. In this way the three-dimensional organization of the mitochondrial membrane would be represented in the amino-acid sequences of the insoluble proteins, and ultimately in the nucleotide sequence of MDNA. Unfortunately for this hypothesis Katoh and Sanukida (1965) could find no differences in the properties of S.P. preparations from wild-type and cytoplasmic 'petite' yeasts. However, it could be that quite subtle changes in binding between S.P. and other mitochondrial proteins would have a profound effect on the formation and activity of the mitochondrion. Also, the interpretation of Katoh and Sanukida's observations is made more difficult by the fact that the 'petite' mitochondrion probably lacks its inner membrane (Yotsuyanagi, 1962).

Most interesting work in this respect has been carried out with *Neurospora crassa* by Munkres and Woodward (see Chapter Seven). Firstly, certain malate-requiring mutants were studied (Munkres and Woodward, 1966). It was found that the differences between the normal and the mutant cells were due not only to changes in the properties of malate dehydrogenase itself but also in the malate dehydrogenase–S.P. complex. Thus the complex isolated from mitochondria of the malate-requiring cell had a much higher Km for malate (i.e. a lower affinity) than the similar complex from the normal. Thus alterations in the binding of proteins to S.P. could affect their activity *in vivo*.

It can be shown that certain respiratory-deficient mutants of *Neurospora crassa* are maternally inherited (see Chapter Seven). In such mutations there are enzymic and chemical changes analogous to those observed in the cytoplasmic 'petites' of yeast. Woodward and Munkres (1966) studied the mitochondrial S.P. in these mutants and found that there had been a genetic amino-acid replacement of the membrane-bound S.P. They suggest that the mutation in S.P. results from alterations in mitochondrial DNA, with resultant replacement of single amino acids in the peptide chain of S.P. such replacement may ultimately disrupt the system for mitochondrial assembly (see Chapter Seven for a more detailed account).

We may conclude that there is reasonable evidence that mitochondrial insoluble proteins are synthesized *in vitro* and that this synthesis reflects processes occurring in the living cell. The amino-acid sequence of these proteins may be encoded in MDNA, and it is reasonable to suppose that alterations in insoluble membrane-bound protein arising from cytoplasmic mutation may well result in drastic effects on the organization and assembly of the mitochondrion. The chemistry of insoluble membrane proteins is still not fully understood, and it is possible that a single insoluble protein (S.P.) is formed. However, it is more likely that a family of such proteins are synthesized. The possibility cannot be ruled out on present evidence that some of these proteins are indeed the apo-enzymes of bound respiratory enzymes, such as cytochromes *a* and *b*, or even ribosomal structural proteins (see p. 107).

General survey of mechanism of mitochondrial protein synthesis
We have seen in this chapter how the mitochondrial system carries out the synthesis of insoluble membrane-bound protein, and how this process is related to the metabolic and structural state of the mitochondrion. The properties and biosynthesis of mitochondrial DNA, and mitochondrial RNA, and the occurrence of ribosomes and SRNA are described in Chapter One. We can also take the results on labelling *in vivo*

described in Chapter Two to give an overall view of the essential properties of the mechanisms for the synthesis of mitochondrial proteins, as we now understand them. A scheme is presented in Fig. 12 which shows the interactions of nuclear DNA, MDNA, cytoplasmic and mito-

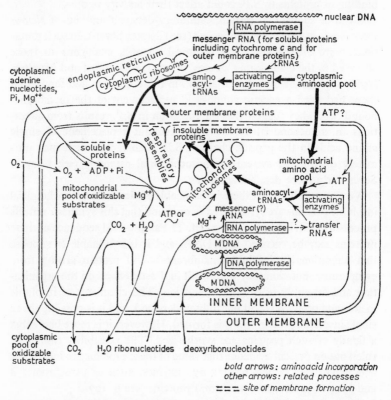

FIG. 12 Probable pathways for synthesis of mitochondrial proteins

chondrial ribosomes and SRNA, activating enzymes, energy generating systems, cytomembranes, and mitochondrial membranes. Some of the details in this figure are established with great certainty, some are tentative, and some even speculative. Nevertheless, the fact that such a scheme can be drawn up at all is a measure of the progress made in the last few years.

CHAPTER FOUR

Evolutionary Origin of Mitochondria

Similarities between bacteria and mitochondria

An extraordinary outcome of the last few years research on amino-acid incorporation by isolated mitochondria, and the discovery of MDNA, is that fifty-year-old ideas of the 'bacterial' origin of the mitochondrion have now suddenly become highly relevant. Lehninger (1964) gives an account of some of these early ideas in his book on the mitochondrion. For example, Altmann spoke in 1890 of mitochondria as the 'elementar organismen', primitive, self-replicating bodies (or 'bioblasts') within the cell. As pointed out by Lehninger, much of the difficulty faced by the present-day biochemist when reading this 'pre-electron microscope' literature arises from the multiplicity of names for mitochondria, caused by the absence of clear criteria for defining the particle.

We will therefore not deal with these early studies here, but instead point to various recent observations and studies that are relevant to this enthralling problem in biology. The most striking occurrence is the discovery of several properties of mitochondria that closely resemble those of bacteria. This suggests that it is possible that mitochondria originated from a primitive bacterium-like organism that invaded a nucleated cell, and developed into an 'endosymbiont'. It may therefore be of some use at this point to discuss the similarities between mitochondria and bacteria. A detailed account of these similarities has recently been given by Nass *et al.* (1965).

The overall dimensions of mitochondria and bacteria are similar, and the rod-shaped bacteria are similar in shape to many types of mitochondria. Although the outer capsule of the bacterial wall is clearly very different from the outer mitochondrial membrane, it is not unreasonable to regard the inner membrane of the mitochondrion as analogous to the bacterial cell membrane. In particular, it is now clear that there are respiratory assemblies organized in a similar way in both the bacterial membrane and the inner mitochondrial membrane (see, e.g., Lascelles, 1966). Indeed, there are many resemblances between the properties of 'respiratory assemblies' that have been isolated from mammalian mitochondria, and bacteria.

There are also resemblances between the lipid composition of mitochondrial membranes and bacterial membranes. Recent studies by many research groups have shown quite clearly that the mitochondrial membrane is highly selective in the substances that can pass through it. Indeed, there are strong indications from current work that there is a 'permease' system in the mitochondrial membrane, similar to that in the bacteria. Yotsuyanagi (1966) has observed myelin figures in yeast mitochondria that greatly resemble the bacterial 'mesosome' (see also Haldar *et al.*, 1966).

We have seen above (Chapter Three) that the synthesis of certain mitochondrial proteins is highly sensitive to certain anti-bacterial drugs, such as chloramphenicol, whereas 'microsomal' protein synthesis is resistant. It is most likely that this sensitivity is due to differences between mitochondrial and cytoplasmic ribosomes. Chloramphenicol appears to bind with 70 S bacterial ribosomes but not with 80 S nonbacterial ribosomes. The indications at the moment are that mitochondrial ribosomes are probably 55–60 S, and would thus more clearly resemble the bacterial systems (see Chapters One and Eight).

The most striking similarity, however, is the circular nature of MDNA (see Chapter One). Indeed, the initial discovery of DNA fibrils in mitochondria lead Nass and Nass (1963) to wonder whether the old theories of the evolution of mitochondria from bacteria should be revived. They observed that the DNA tended to lie in a central region of the mitochondrion which was analogous to the 'nucleoid' region of bacteria. It is striking that hitherto circular DNA molecules had only been found in micro-organisms, and there was no indication of circularity in the DNA of higher organisms, particularly mammals. It is also most interesting that analysis of the nearest-neighbour frequencies of mitochondrial DNA showed similarities with bacterial DNA (Cummins *et al.*, 1967). To quote these authors: 'These results suggest that mitochondrial DNA may be, in terms of evolution, more closely related to bacterial DNA than it is to the chromosomal DNA of higher organisms.'

The discovery of DNA polymerase, RNA polymerase, SRNA, activating enzymes, ribosomes, and amino-acid incorporation activity in isolated mitochondria all point to the presence of reasonably autonomous replicative apparatus that is similar in its essentials to that of a free-living micro-organism. There is no requirement for complex cytoplasmic factors (such as added SRNA or activating enzymes), and mitochondrial amino-acid incorporation takes place in relatively simple media that could well be bacterial growth media.

Thus in general morphology, enzyme localization, chemical constitution, drug sensitivity, nucleic acid structure, and protein-synthesizing machinery there are striking similarities between mitochondria and bacteria.

Some indirect arguments
These resemblances are indeed powerful and give strong force to an 'endosymbiotic theory'. However, there are more indirect arguments which may, or may not, be relevant. If mitochondria arose by 'infection' of a primitive nucleated cell with bacteria-like organisms, one might well expect some diversity in the mitochondrial population, even in the same host since it would be most unlikely that only one strain of 'bacterium' was infective. Recently Avers, Rancourt, and Lin (1965) used electron microscopy and enzyme histochemistry to show that certain yeast mutants contained mixed populations of mitochondria, some with cytochrome oxidase and some without. They argued that if 'different mitochondria co-existed in the same cell, it would indicate some autonomous control of organelle phenotype'. There have indeed been continuous reports in the literature of heterogeneity in the mitochondrial population of mammalian liver, and recently Swick, Stange, Nance, and Thomson (1967) have confirmed this by careful enzymic and centrifugal analysis of mitochondrial populations of rat liver. Many so-called 'mitochondrial' enzymes also occur in the soluble phase of the cell. The interesting aspect of such 'dual localization' is that in most cases it appears that the enzyme in the soluble phase has not merely escaped from the mitochondria during cell fractionation but is in fact a different protein. (For a fuller account see Roodyn, 1967.) The best example is malate dehydrogenase, where it has been established without doubt that the mitochondrial and cytoplasmic enzymes are

different proteins. It is therefore rather surprising that the cell should synthesize two different sets of enzymes that have very similar functions. However, if we imagine that the cytoplasmic enzymes were those in the original host cell, and the mitochondrial enzymes were in the original infective 'bacterium', the reason for this situation becomes clear.

The question of the properties and biosynthesis of the inner and outer mitochondrial membrane is relevant. There are now strong indications that the inner and outer membranes are made by different mechanisms. The outer membrane also has certain close similarities in its enzymic constitution to microsomal membranes (Sottocasa, Kuylenstierna, Ernster, and Bergstrand, 1967).

The synthesis of the inner membrane appears to be sensitive to the action of chloramphenicol, is affected by cytoplasmic mutation, and is the major site of amino-acid incorporation *in vitro*. It is thus quite reasonable to suppose that the synthesis of the inner membrane is under the control of MDNA, whereas the outer membrane is under more direct nuclear control. This is precisely the situation that would arise if the inner membrane had evolved from the primitive 'bacterial' membrane, which has been enclosed in an outer membrane derived from the host cell.

If mitochondria arose from infective aerobic micro-organisms, one might well ask how the host cell survived in an aerobic environment before infection. What was the respiratory system of the host cell before it accepted the 'endosymbiont'? Here we must introduce some recent important discoveries of de Duve, Baudhuin, Berthet, Beaufay, and their colleagues. They have established that the so-called 'microbodies' found in mammalian liver in fact belong to a general class of particles called 'peroxisomes' (see de Duve and Baudhuin, 1966, for a recent review). The term 'peroxisome' was used since the enzymes discovered in these particles either formed or decomposed hydrogen peroxide. They were D amino-acid oxidase, urate oxidase, L-α-hydroxy acid oxidase, and catalase. In their general article on the subject de Duve and Baudhuin (1966) propose a scheme whereby these enzymes acting concertedly could provide a mechanism for non-mitochondrial oxidation of NADH. They point out that the enzyme D amino-acid oxidase, which is anomolous because it attacks D amino acids rather than the normal L series, has been called a 'fossil' enzyme, i.e. it represents some 'vestigial' enzymic path for the oxidation of substances that now are no longer of general occurrence in the cell. In some very interesting speculation, they wonder whether this concept should not be extended to the whole peroxisome. Perhaps it is a 'fossil' respiratory particle that may have been active in cells in early evolution. It would therefore be very tempting to imagine that the original nucleated host cell survived under aerobic conditions because it contained peroxisomes. After infection of the cell with aerobic micro-organisms, the peroxisomes lost many of their functions, and we are now presented with only vestigial particles. It will therefore be most interesting to follow future developments in our knowledge of the distribution of peroxisomes in different cell types.

Implications of the endosymbiont theory

Sagan (1967) has surveyed many aspects of this question in a most learned and stimulating article. Biochemical, cytological, taxonomic, and palaentological evidence are all knit together in support of the thesis that in addition to primitive protozoan cells, the three 'fundamental organelles' [mitochondria, photosynthetic plastids, and basal bodies of the (9 + 2) flagellae] were 'once free-living prototrophic cells'. It is proposed, for example, that protozoan cells symbiotically acquired photosynthetic plastids giving rise to the eukaryotic algae, and hence green plants.

In the particular case of mitochondria, Sagan finds that they satisfy many of the following criteria laid down by her for proposing that an organelle arose as an endosymbiont.

1. The organelle must have once been able to replicate DNA and its own protein-synthesizing apparatus. In current biochemical terms this would include DNA, messenger RNA (MRNA) complimentary to this DNA, a functional system for protein synthesis, a source of ATP and other nucleotides, a source of other small molecules for protein and nucleic acid synthesis, and a system for elaborating cell membranes. To quote Sagan directly: '. . . Upon entry into a host, such a symbiont may lose from some to all of its synthetic capabilities, *except the ability to replicate its own DNA* and synthesize complimentary mRNA from that DNA, the *sine qua non* of any organism.'

E

2. The daughter cell must receive at least one copy of the genome of the symbiont.

3. One would not expect to find 'intermediate intracellular stages' of the organelle. It would either be present or absent.

4. If the symbiont is lost, there would be a concomitant loss of all metabolic characteristics coded by the genome of the symbiont.

5. The symbiont will show non-Mendelian genetics. (By this, of course, is meant that the inheritance of symbiont characteristics will not show classical segregation and recombination with nuclear genes of the host cell. It may show Mendelian genetics within its own system, however, if symbiont units can segregate and be considered as a separate population.)

6. It should be possible to find 'naturally occurring counterparts' among organisms that exist at the present time.

The reader may not agree with all these criteria, or may indeed feel that they are insufficient. Nevertheless, it is most striking that most of these criteria appear to be met to a greater or lesser extent by mitochondria. Perhaps it is for the reader to judge, from the evidence presented in this book, how far, for example, criteria 3, 4, and 6 are met (the 'natural counterpart' in criterion 6 would, of course, be an aerobic bacterium). Criteria 1, 2, and 5 seem to the authors, at least, to be fully satisfied.

Possible stages in mitochondrial evolution
There is inevitably a great speculative element in any discussions on the evolution of living systems. However, it is now clear that the answer to these questions can come only from the integration of findings in many fields of science. These must at least include biochemistry, genetics, cytology, taxonomy, microbiology, and palaentology. In these days of intense specialization in the sciences, the need for the 'overall view' becomes more pressing. Let us hope that the impelling challenge to research workers to resolve these fascinating problems will break down the artificial barriers that separate one branch of human knowledge from the other. Sagan's article is certainly a great advance in this direction. To conclude this chapter we will summarize the major events in mitochondrial evolution as postulated by Sagan, and also present some evidence about the evolution of cytochrome *c*.

The following stages are suggested:

1. Primitive prokaryotic cells evolved about 3,000–5,000 million years ago when the earth's atmosphere was *reducing* in nature, and consisted of hydrogen, nitrogen, water, methane, and traces of ammonia and carbon dioxide.

2. Two types of prokaryotic cell then evolved. One developed a primitive photosynthetic system, and the other ('anaerobic respirers') developed a primitive respiratory system using, perhaps, nitrate and sulphate as electron acceptors. The development of the first type of cell lead to the increased release of oxygen into the atmosphere, as the result of photosynthetic activity.

3. This enabled the 'anaerobic respirers' to evolve the final step in the respiratory chain, and oxidize carbohydrate completely to carbon dioxide and water. They thus became 'aerobic respirers' or 'promitochondria'.

4. The next major step resulted from the increasing concentration of oxygen in the earth's atmosphere, oxygen becoming abundant about 1,200 million years ago. All cells had to become increasingly adapted to the aerobic environment. Also, the appearance of ozone in the upper atmosphere cut off ultraviolet radiation, and hence prevented the 'abiogenic' formation of life from inorganic matter. All forms of life thus became dependent, directly or indirectly, on photosynthesis. To survive, heterotrophs were forced to eat organic matter derived from photosynthetic or chemi-autotrophic organisms.

5. The evolution of ingestion mechanisms for this process thus made it possible for an anaerobic heterotrophic cell to ingest a promitochondrion without killing it. The resultant symbiotic relationship was a great advantage to the heterotrophic cell, since it was then supplied with an active aerobic system for energy supply. In addition, it is possible that the symbiotic relationship allowed the cell to develop more complex intracellular membranes, such as the nuclear membrane and the endoplasmic reticulum, and it also made amoeboid movement possible.

6. Sagan then deals with the evolution of the mitotic system, and the incorporation of flagellate organisms into the primitive heterotrophe. However, from the point of view of mitochondrial evolution,

we may simply say that from about 1,000 million years ago the primitive amoeboid cell developed in (5) evolved into an ancestral eukaryotic cell, which developed a mitotic system, and ultimately gave rise to eukaryotic fungi, protozoans, and animals.

The detailed mechanism of evolution of the various mitochondrial assemblies, in particular those in the cristae, is of course very much a matter for speculation. Perhaps the lines of future investigation will be on the basis of a most interesting paper by Margoliash (1963) on the evolution of cytochrome c. The amino-acid sequences of purified cytochrome c from horse, man, pig, rabbit, chicken, tuna, and baker's yeast were compared. In general, remarkable similarities were found between the sequences. The differences were most marked in cytochrome c molecules from phylogenetically different species, and closely related species showed little differences. For example, horse and pig cytochromes showed only three variations in sequence, whereas there were forty-four differences between horse and yeast cytochrome c. From palaentological evidence as to the date of divergence of the evolution of horse and man, and from differences in the amino-acid sequences of human and horse haemoglobin, it has been calculated that an average of 11 million years is required for a mutation to occur that gives rise to a difference of one amino acid in the polypeptide chains. Although it is possibly hazardous to assume that the rates of mutation of all proteins have been the same in evolutionary history, Margoliash used this method to calculate the approximate dates at which the various proteins (and by implication, different mitochondria) diverged from a primordial stock. Thus the divergency between yeast and the various animals studied appeared to take place about 500 million years ago. It is most encouraging that this could well fit into Sagan's scheme, and would correspond to the divergence of the ancestral eukaryotic cell into fungi, on the one hand, and precursors of animal cells, on the other. It is thus quite possible that our ever-increasing knowledge of the primary structure of proteins will reveal exciting glimpses of the ancestral history of the mitochondrion.

CHAPTER FIVE

Cellular Site and Mechanism of Assembly of Mitochondria

Role of the nucleus

In this chapter we will discuss the question of the cellular site of mito-chondrial formation. Many different parts of the cell have been im-plicated in mitochondrial formation, and it is, regrettably, difficult at the moment to decide conclusively which view is correct. (For a detailed account of this problem see Novikoff, 1961.) We will consider the nucleus first. There is strong evidence that the nuclear genes have considerable control over the formation of mitochondria (Chapter Six). At the moment we do not know whether the control is by the passage of messenger RNA into the cytoplasm or whether some sort of mito-chondrial precursor is actually formed in or near the nucleus. There are many indications of some sort of relationship between the nuclear membrane and mitochondria. For example, North and Pollak (1961) found that mitochondria appeared to be grouped more closely around the nuclear membrane during the embryonic development of chick liver than in the adult. Several workers have reported apparent continuity between mitochondria and the nuclear membrane. Hartman (1954) suggested that mitochondria arise from 'sub-microscopic granules' near the nucleo-cytoplasmic interface in nerve cells, rather than by division of existing mitochondria.

There have been other reports of apparent formation of mitochondria from nuclear structures. Steinert (1960) suggested formation of mito-chondria from the trypanosome kinetonucleus. In more recent studies, Bell and Mühlethaler (1962) followed the maturation of fern egg cells. They suggested that mitochondria arose from evaginations into the cytoplasm arising from the nuclear membrane. In an interesting study of embryonic rat liver by Dadoune (1963) it was shown that mito-chondria appear to be very close to the nuclear membrane in the liver of the new-born rat. In one section a mitochondrion was observed that was apparently fused to the nuclear membrane. This may indicate formation from nuclear material, but may also be an artifact arising from the sectioning procedure. In all these studies the problems of interpretation of thin sections are great. For example, it has been shown that flattenings on the surface of the mitochondrion can give rise to many artifacts in thin sections.

We can thus summarize by saying that there is good genetic evidence for nuclear control of mitochondrial formation, and some cytological evidence implying a direct role of nuclear structures, in particular the membrane.

Microbodies

The history of the study of mitochondrial biogenesis contains many false trails. Perhaps a good example of this is the supposed role of 'microbodies'. In 1956 Rouiller and Bernhard made a careful electron-microscope study of regenerating liver and the other tissues and dis-covered a series of single-membraned structures which resembled a primitive form of mitochondrion. They called these 'microbodies' and suggested that they were precursors of mitochondria. Although this view was disputed by Novikoff (1961), it was accepted by many workers for some years. (The role of microbodies is also discussed by Bade, 1964.) Recently, however, it has been clearly established by the Louvain group that microbodies have a totally different enzymic constitution to mitochondria, and are in fact concerned in peroxide metabolism ('peroxisomes' – see Chapter Four).

One should conclude from this work that cytological examination, *by itself*, can give most misleading answers to problems of cell development. de Duve (1967) has pointed out the necessity of enzymic analysis of cell structures for a true appreciation of their properties: 'the impact of enzyme cytology on descriptive morphology is hardly less important. We need only think of how sterile our vision of even the most beautiful present-day electron micrographs would be, were it not illuminated, sometimes even by direct cytochemical illustration, by our knowledge of the enzymic attributes of intracellular structures.'

It is for this reason that any theory of mitochondrial biogenesis must provide not only a *visual* explanation of the processes involved but also a chemical and enzymic analysis of the stages involved.

Role of cytomembranes

There is also good evidence that the cytomembrane system is involved in mitochondrial formation (for a description of this system see Reid, 1967). Dadoune (1963) observed that there was frequently a close relationship between mitochondria and the endoplasmic reticulum in embryonic rat liver. He raised the possibility that the 'ergastoplasm' may participate in the formation of mitochondria. There have also been suggestions that Golgi cytomembranes are involved in mitochondrial formation. In a paper that discussed the general problem of mitochondrial biogenesis, Schjeide, McCandless, and Munn (1964) suggested that mitochondria arise from 'mitochondria-like organelles' that have a double membrane but rudimentary cristae. The cristae are formed by fusion of 'microvesicles'. Robertson suggested that mitochondria may arise by differentiation of cytomembranes, and has also proposed that invaginations of the bounding cell membrane itself may give rise to mitochondria (Robertson, 1959).

Many of these studies are really, at the best, only circumstantial in their conclusions. However, Bade (1964) has made a more conclusive study. The appearance of mitochondria in regenerating mouse liver was followed by electron microscopy. Bade observed a progressive transformation of elements of the endoplasmic reticulum cisternae into double membranes and cristae, characteristic of mitochondria. At one stage in this process an intermediate structure was formed which was neither cytomembrane nor mitochondrion, and Bade called it a 'promitochondrium'. During the regenerative process many mitochondria with incomplete outer membranes were observed, and they were often found to be in close association with the endoplasmic reticulum. Other workers have also argued that the differentiation of membranes has a role in mitochondrial formation. For example, Robertis and Bleichmar (1962) suggested that mitochondria in nerve fibres arise by differentiation of a pair of parallel membranes arising from the axolemma.

Recently biochemical investigations have strongly implicated membrane (microsomal) systems in the biosynthesis of mitochondrial proteins, in particular cytochrome *c* (see Chapter Two). There have been some interesting direct experiments by Kadenbach (1967a), using mixed mitochondrial and microsomal systems. Unlabelled mitochondria were incubated with a microsomal fraction that had been labelled *in vitro*. It was found that radioactive protein was transferred from the microsomal to the mitochondrial fraction. The transfer was dependent on the physical integrity of the microsomal fraction, since there was no transfer with solubilized microsomal proteins alone. The reaction is slow, energy-dependent, and probably requires GTP. It probably takes place by a process of physical binding of microsomal material to the mitochondrion. Kadenbach suggests that similar processes take place within the living cell, i.e. material is passed in some way from the cyto-membrane system to the mitochondrion during its formation. Very recently Kadenbach (1967b) has claimed that the synthesis of cyto-chrome *c in vitro* can be demonstrated with such mixed mitochondrial-microsomal systems. It may well be, therefore, that these artificially reconstructed systems do resemble systems *in vivo* quite closely.

Formation of mitochondria in yeast

An extreme example of changes in the structure and enzymic constitu-tion of the mitochondrion that can occur in the living cell is seen in the profound alterations that occur during respiratory adaptation in faculta-tive anaerobic yeasts, such as *Saccharomyces cerevisiae*. The yeast cell grown under strictly anaerobic conditions by using fermentation as an energy source is free of functional mitochondria, and the bulk of the respiratory system, including the essential terminal oxidase cytochrome oxidase, is absent. On admission of oxygen to the culture there is a rapid induction of respiratory enzymes, oxygen uptake is greatly sti-mulated, and eventually mitochondria are formed in the cytoplasm. Clearly such a system is of great experimental use, and there is now a large literature on the biochemistry and cytology of respiratory adapta-tion in yeast. The major early findings on the essential properties of the system are discussed in lectures by Ephrussi (1950) and Slonimski (1956), as well as the relationship of these findings to the formation of respiratory-deficient mutants (see Chapter Six). The induction of respiratory enzymes occurs fairly rapidly, and within about ten hours the cells have developed normal respiratory activity, at least with glucose as an energy source. We will see shortly, however, that appearance of oxygen uptake is not a rigorous measure of the rate of formation of mitochondria.

Since anaerobic cells lack a family of respiratory enzymes and possess no active mitochondria, one can infer that oxygen is required for the formation of the respiratory system. However, there has been some dispute about this, for the following technical reason. In order to grow cells anaerobically, one must provide an energy source. The most convenient is glucose, which can be fermented to ethanol and carbon dioxide by the classical glycolysis pathway. However, glucose is a powerful repressor of the synthesis of the respiratory system (see Chapter Six). The absence of mitochondria in the anaerobic cell grown on glucose may therefore be due to severe glucose repression. Tustanoff and Bartley (1964) indeed found that if galactose was used as an energy source (this sugar does not appear to repress) it was possible to grow, anaerobically, cells which had respiratory activity, including cytochrome oxidase. Somlo and Fukuhara (1965), however, repeated this work with extreme precautions to remove all traces of oxygen, and added a protein synthesis inhibitor during the harvesting of the cells, to prevent respiratory adaptation occurring. They found that galactose-grown cells were indeed deficient in a range of respiratory enzymes. It thus appears that the respiratory system can be induced readily by low concentrations of molecular oxygen. The oxygen requirement appears to be specific, and respiratory adaptation cannot be induced with other electron acceptors. Since the anaerobic cell is virtually free of cytochrome oxidase, which is the site of interaction of the respiratory chain with molecular oxygen, it is clear that the 'sensor' for intracellular levels of oxygen during respiratory adaptation cannot be the classical respiratory system of flavoproteins and cytochromes arranged in a mitochondrial-like structure. However, there are non-mitochondrial enzyme systems that react with oxygen, and one of these must be involved. In relation to the question of the precise effect of oxygen, it is interesting that mitochondrial protein synthesis *in vitro* appears to be highly dependent on adequate aeration of the suspension. Thus oxygen may act not only by inducing the synthesis of respiratory enzymes but also by directly influencing the rate of mitochondrial protein synthesis (Roodyn, 1966a).

The changes of enzyme constitution that occur during respiratory adaptation are quite complex. For example, there appear to be several lactate dehyrogenases in yeast, with different substrate and electron acceptor affinities. During respiratory adaptation anaerobic lactate dehydrogenase disappears, and several aerobic dehydrogenases appear (see, e.g., Singer, Gregolin, and Cremona, 1963). The most striking changes occur in the cytochrome system, however. Anaerobic cells are not devoid of cytochromes but in fact contain small amounts of two haem proteins absorbing at 556 mμ and 585–590 mμ (cytochromes b_1 and a_1: Ephrussi and Slonimski, 1950). During respiratory adapatation these disappear, and are replaced by the 'classical' cytochromes of the respiratory chain: b, c, c_1, a, and a_3 (see, e.g., Lindenmayer and Estabrook, 1958). The biosynthetic relationship between the anaerobic and aerobic cytochromes is certainly quite complex, with probable common precursor substances. Although respiratory activity appears fairly rapidly after admission of oxygen, it is certain that not all the mitochondrial enzymes are synthesized simultaneously. For example, cytochrome oxidase appears to be induced before succinate dehydrogenase (Slonimski, 1956). Also, Polakis, Bartley, and Meek (1964) found that the ability to oxidize glucose and ethanol appeared after twelve hours of adaptation, but the cells could not oxidize acetate until there had been twelve hours more in oxygen (see below). The sequence of synthesis of the various respiratory enzymes may therefore give us a useful indication of the sequence of assembly of the mitochondrion.

It is interesting that respiratory adaptation can occur in quite simple media, and in non-growing cells. The mitochondria appear to be assembled from endogenous building blocks, without any great demand on the biosynthetic activity of the cell. Thus Fukuhara (1967) found that the overall rates of protein synthesis in adapted and non-adapted cells were very similar. Only a small proportion of the total cellular protein showed a higher rate of labelling during respiratory adaptation. Also, Bartley and Tustanoff (1966) found that respiratory adaptation was not markedly affected by a variety of inhibitors of glycolysis, RNA synthesis, and protein synthesis, and they concluded that the mitochondria were not formed by new synthesis from low molecular weight compounds. They suggested that cytochrome oxidase, for example, may be present in the anaerobic cell as a non-functional apoenzyme, and during adaptation merely acquire porphyrin and metal to become enzymically active. The same may apply to other respiratory enzymes. There is therefore the possibility that mitochondria are formed either partially or completely from structurally organized precursors. Indeed, there is considerable evidence that membranous structures, which we may call in general terms 'promitochondrial membranes', are involved in the synthesis of yeast mitochondria. Linnane, Vitols, and Nowland (1962) showed that in the yeast *Torulopsis utilis*, mitochondria appear to arise from membranous elements that contain certain 'primary' mitochondrial enzymes, such as succinate dehydrogenase, but no cytochromes. It was suggested that these 'reticular membranes' are present in anaerobic cells and differentiate into mature mitochondria on aeration of the cells. Polakis *et al.* (1964) found that the formation of mitochondria during respiratory adaptation was preceded by the formation of vesicular structures. Cells containing these structures could oxidize glucose and ethanol, but not acetate. Only after twenty-four hours of adaptation could the cells oxidize acetate, and it was then that mitochondria appeared. Thus non-mitochondrial respiratory structures appeared to be formed as an initial stage in mitochondrial biogenesis. The formation of vesicles preceding the appearance of mitochondria was also observed by Wallace and Linnane (1964), in a study of the cytology and enzymology of respiratory adaptation.

These observations are confirmed by the work of Schatz (1965). Yeast cells harvested at various stages of respiratory adaptation were homogenized and fractionated by differential centrifugation by using suitable density gradients. It was found that membranous elements form before the appearance of intact mitochondria. These membranes contain certain mitochondrial enzymes, such as Mg^{++} activated ATPase. It was therefore suggested that the anaerobic cell contains 'promitochondria' which differentiate into mitochondria during respiratory adaptation. These structures are thought of as being analogous to 'proplastids' which give rise to chloroplasts in the light.

Related to the changes in respiratory adaptation is the effect of glucose on mitochondrial formation in yeast. The so-called 'glucose repression' has been the subject of many detailed studies (see Chapter Six). Essentially, growth of yeast in the presence of glucose results in severe modification in the appearance of mitochondria and reduction in their number (see, e.g., Polakis *et al.*, 1965). As the glucose is converted to ethanol, one reaches a point in the growth conditions in which the glucose concentration falls to a level which can no longer cause repression. At the same time the cells begin to oxidize the ethanol, and the number of mitochondria per cell increase. This process may be called 'de-repression'.

As we have discussed in Chapter Two, Jayaraman *et al.* (1966) have recently studied the processes that occur during glucose de-repression. They concluded that the mitochondria do not appear to arise *de novo* from free proteins, nucleic acids, and lipids, but are formed by the aggregation of organized membrane structures that contain some, but not all, of the constituents of the mitochondrion.

It is thus reasonably certain that in facultative anaerobes the process of formation of new mitochondria occurs by the aggregation and differentiation of membranous precursors. There is also suggestive evidence that similar processes occur in higher cells.

de novo *synthesis; mitochondrial growth and division*

Many early experiments by a variety of workers on egg cells had suggested that mitochondria could arise *de novo*, that is to say, from parts of cells that had no mitochondria, or obvious mitochondrial precursors. However, as discussed more fully by Lehninger (1964), this early work (in particular that of Beckwith and Harvey) on mitochondrial formation was carried out with the relatively poor resolving power of the light microscope, and was very dependent on specific staining reactions. Subsequent work with the electron microscope has shown, unfortunately, that many of the conclusions drawn with light microscopy alone are not valid (see Novikoff, 1961). Thus, in this particular case, it was shown that the so-called 'mitochondria-free' preparations in fact do contain mitochondria. Thus in egg cells the mitochondria are readily obscured by excessive lipid (see, e.g., Berg and Humphreys, 1960).

However, some electron-microscopy work has indicated that mitochondria may arise *de novo* in certain conditions. For example, Berger (1964) found mitochondrial structures in various stages of development in photoreceptor retinal cells. From his studies he concluded that mitochondria in fact arise *de novo* in the cytoplasm near the nuclear membrane. Also, in the study of developmental changes in the oocyte, Adams and Hertig (1964) observed that mitochondria appeared to develop from regions free of mitochondria. It was also interesting that they developed in characteristic 'clusters' or 'rosettes'. The centre of the rosette consisted of a dense 'core', possibly of ribonucleoprotein or lipoprotein.

In contrast to these indications that mitochondria may arise from non-mitochondrial, and possibly molecular, precursors, there is also considerable evidence that mitochondria, once formed, can grow and possibly divide. These two viewpoints are not necessarily contradictory. Thus the *formation* of mitochondria may well proceed by one mechanism and the growth and replication of the fully formed mitochondrion by another. There is certainly overwhelming evidence that mitochondria are not static structures, but alter their position, size, shape, and even fine structure quite readily. Space does not allow a detailed treatment of all cases of mitochondrial alteration in the living cell, and only a few examples will be given to illustrate the extreme plasticity of the 'chondriome'.

Phase-contrast cinematography of a wide range of cells has revealed many changes in size, shape, and position (see, e.g., Ritchie and Hazeltine, 1953). Frederic (1958) carried out a most comprehensive study of the alterations in the appearance and position of mitochondria in tissue culture cells observed by cinematography. These alterations were found to occur in a wide variety of conditions, and the reader is strongly recommended to read this paper in order to appreciate the falseness of a 'static' view of the mitochondrion. Massive changes in mitochondrial structure and packing occur during the formation of the sperm. There are also drastic changes in mitochondria during the development of the retina, and when trypanosomes are transferred from the mammal to the fly (Vickermann, 1963). We have mentioned above the mitochondrial hypertrophy that can occur in the hyperthyroid animal, and the mitochondrion is indeed profoundly affected by the hormonal status of the animal. It is also changed in many pathological states (see Mugnaini, 1964b). We have discussed in detail above the profound changes that can occur in the number and fine structure of mitochondria in yeast grown under different conditions.

There is electron-microscopic evidence for mitochondrial growth and division, although it is perhaps not yet absolutely rigorous. For example, Mugnaini (1964b) found that some mitochondria in preparations of human liver showed clear projections or buds. Frequently two fused mitochondria were observed with either an incomplete or complete septum between them. Also some giant mitochondria were observed. Brosemer, Vogell, and Bücher (1963) found that locust flight-muscle mitochondria could increase sixty times in size during growth of the muscle. At no time was there any sudden change in enzyme composition, indicating that mitochondria are growing continuously. Brosemer and co-workers concluded that it was unlikely that mitochondria were made from 'ghosts' or by differentiation of non-mitochondrial membranes. Electron micrographs of mitochondria in partial or complete division have been reported by a number of workers (e.g. Fawcett, 1955; Maltzahn and Mühlethaler, 1962; and Mugnaini, 1964b). Bahr and Zeitler (1962) made a quantitative study of mitochondrial populations in rat liver under the electron microscope and concluded as well that it was very likely that mitochondria divide. The division is not necessarily symmetrical, however. They also concluded that mitochondria increase in size by linear growth prior to division.

We may at this point remind the reader of the labelling experiments *in vivo* described in Chapter Two. In particular, the experiments of Luck with *Neurospora crassa* indicated that there was continuous growth and division of the mitochondrion, rather than discontinuous formation from non-mitochondrial precursors at restricted phases of the cell cycle. There thus seems reasonable evidence that the mitochondrion can grow, differentiate, bud, and probably divide *in vivo*. However, since there is also good evidence that not all the mitochondrial proteins (in particular cytochrome *c*) are made *in situ*, we have to assume that during the process of growth and differentiation, components that are made in non-mitochondrial sites are somehow transferred across the mito-chondrial membrane. As mentioned above, Kadenbach (1967a, b) has recently studied such phenomena by direct experiments *in vitro*, and has concluded that there is, indeed, an energy-linked transfer of protein from microsomal membranes to mitochondria.

Finally, it may be pointed out very briefly that considerable changes take place in the mitochondrial population and enzyme levels during embryonic development, and an account of some of these alterations during amphibian development may be found in Deuchar (1966).

Molecular mechanism of mitochondrial assembly

Such an approach leads us to a direct and very exciting field of study. This is the attempt to assemble a mitochondrion *in vitro* from its component parts. It has been known for many years that the respiratory chain can be 'reconstituted' if appropriate 'respiratory complexes' isolated from it are brought together in the test-tube. The technical difficulties and possible errors in such reconstitution experiments are discussed in Chapter Four of Lehninger's book on the mitochondrion (Lehninger, 1964). Nevertheless, they do constitute a rather daring approach to the problem. Recently Tzagoloff, MacLennan, McConnell, and Green (1967) have observed the formation of membranes during reconstitution of the mitochondrial respiratory system. It is difficult at the moment to assess the full significance of these observations, but they certainly raise the possibility that mitochondria may indeed form 'spontaneously' by the polymerization of suitable building blocks or precursors. There is little doubt that such precursors cannot simply be free proteins, nucleic acids, and lipids, but must in fact be rather complex sub-units with a considerable degree of internal organization. It is likely that such sub-units are bound together by suitable structural (or 'organizer') proteins and interact with each other at specific binding sites, of an as yet unknown nature.

It may seem to the reader that it is most improbable that a structure as complex as the mitochondrion can simply 'come together' from its constituent sub-units. This may well be true, and the test-tube reconstitution of an intact mitochondrion may be a hopeless dream. However, structures of some degree of complexity have recently been shown to assemble, *in vitro* from relatively simple precursors (e.g. bacterial flagellae and certain viruses). The formation of bacterial flagellae results from the polymerization of a single protein of molecular weight 30,000–40,000 (flagellin), and can readily be observed *in vitro* (e.g. Asakura and Eguchi, 1964). The reconstitution *in vitro* of complex viruses has also been described (e.g. Israel, Anderson, and Levine, 1967). In some very interesting experiments using artificial mixtures of lecithin, cholesterol, and saponin, Lucy and Glauert (1964) observed the formation of lamellae, tubules, hexagonal and even helical structures. Thus quite remarkable ordered structures can be formed by spontaneous aggregation of quite simple sub-units. Lucy and Glauert suggested that these structures arose by aggregation of globular micelles, and it could well be that mitochondria are formed by a similar process.

Razin, Morowitz, and Terry (1965) studied the membrane of the pleuropneumonia-like organism *Mycoplasma laidlawii*. The membrane was lysed with detergent, and the suspension was found to contain homogeneous lipoprotein sub-units. In suitable media these sub-units spontaneously re-aggregated to form membrane-like structures that retained NADH oxidase activity present in the original intact membrane. The relevance of such observations to mitochondrial formation is clear.

The problems involved in the assembly of the mitochondrial membrane are discussed in a most interesting article by Green and Hechter (1965). They think it unlikely that the sub-units themselves are formed by spontaneous self-assembly, and point out some of the difficulties in imagining that the whole process of mitochondrial formation is directly controlled by 'polysome units'. As a result of their considerations, Green and Hechter propose that special 'templates' exist for the assembly of individual complexes. The authors reach a very interesting conclusion, or prediction, that is well in line with current research on the biosynthesis of mitochondrial proteins. To quote: '. . . this view *demands* that genetic information for membrane formation be transmitted through *two* sets of messenger RNA's, one carrying information for the synthesis of specific protein components of the membrane, the other for the synthesis of proteins to serve as templates for the assembly of membrane units'. We could assume that the first set is messenger RNA molecules synthesized on the nuclear DNA, and the second set messenger RNA made by mitochondrial RNA polymerase on MDNA. The nuclear 'message' could control the synthesis of the individual molecular components of the mitochondrion, while the mitochondrial 'message' could control the synthesis of insoluble proteins that (*a*) bind the molecules together to form sub-units, and (*b*) assemble the sub-units into a complete mitochondrion. If there is indeed any truth in such a scheme, the demonstration of mitochondrial assembly *in vitro* from suitable sub-units may well be achieved in the not too distant future.

Genetic and Regulatory Aspects

PART TWO

Control and Regulatory Aspects

CHAPTER SIX

Respiratory System in Yeast

Regulation of the respiratory system in yeast

Many yeasts are facultative anaerobes and under conditions of anoxia there is inhibition of cytochromes synthesis, energy being provided solely by fermentative breakdown of substrates. Also, it has long been known that glucose acts as a repressor of the respiratory system (Crabtree, 1929), but the mechanism of repression is unknown. Apparently repression is of haem biosynthesis (Sukarada and Matsumura, 1966). Lemoigne *et al.* (1954) studied growth rates of *Saccharomyces cerevisiae* under aerobic conditions in the presence of high concentrations of glucose and found an initial phase of fast growth involving intensive fermentation followed by slow growth by respiration. Separation into these two distinct phases of growth did not occur at low levels of glucose, leading to the conclusion that glucose concentration determines breakdown pathway. In a more detailed analysis, Slominski (1956) found that at very low levels of glucose (less than 6×10^{-3}M), rate of adaptation to respiration increased with increase in glucose concentration, but at levels higher than 6×10^{-3}M, increasing glucose concentration had a delaying effect on the onset of respiratory activity. At the low levels of the sugar the relatively rapid appearance of respiration probably reflects the energy requirements of cells severely restricted by limited amounts of substrate. Continuing these studies, Ephrussi *et al.* (1956) measured rate of fermentation (Q_{CO_2}) and rate of respiration (Q_{O_2}) during aerobic growth of a culture of *S. cerevisiae* starting with cells fully adapted to aerobic conditions and in the presence of 3 per cent glucose. They found that fermentation rate increases markedly during log phase, while Q_{O_2} drops to a low level at the same time. At late log phase when glucose becomes limiting, Q_{CO_2} drops to a low value with a simultaneous increase in Q_{O_2}. Using essentially the same system,

Yotsuyanagi (1962) made electron-microscope studies of cells in different phases of growth and was able to correlate the elaboration of mitochondria with the onset of respiration.

Reilly and Sherman (1965) looked at cytochromes spectra and made Q_{O_2} determinations in *S. cerevisiae* grown with various carbon sources. They report that glucose in very high concentrations (30 per cent) did not block completely the formation of cytochromes and that all bands were present although very weak. They saw no evidence of catabolite repression by melibiose or raffinose, and conclude that melibiose is the best fermentable sugar to use for obtaining de-repressed yeast.

In manometric studies of exponentially growing *S. cerevisiae*, De Deken (1966) finds that degradation of mannose and galactose can proceed simultaneously through fermentation and respiration, although these carbon and energy sources effect a partial repression of the respiratory system. Although cells grow at much the same rate on glucose, fructose, mannose, or galactose during log phase, rates of aerobic fermentation decrease five-fold going from glucose to galactose, while simultaneous rates of respiration increase four-fold from glucose to galactose. Since respiration rate correlates with presence or absence of cytochromes *a*, *b*, and *c*, as determined spectroscopically, the high rates of respiration during growth on mannose and galactose presumably result from *de-repression* of cytochromes synthesis. It was found that the fermentation rates of mannose and galactose are slow compared to glucose in the respiratory-deficient mutant petite (see below), that is, respiration does not regulate fermentation. De Deken concluded that in normal cells it is fermentation rate that regulates respiration rate. Results of further experiments indicate that it is not the shortage of intermediary metabolites (sugar degradation products) that allows de-repression of the respiratory system when fermentation rate is low, but rather the shortage of ATP.

In a recent microscope study of several different yeasts, McClary and Bowers (1967) found a clear correlation between glucose repressibility and instability of mitochondria. Obligate aerobes which are not subject to glucose repression showed a much greater stability of mitochondria structure to alterations in physiological conditions.

Repression of the mitochondrial system by anoxia has been dealt with in Chapter Three. One of the main points is that MDNA is depleted from the cell during anaerobic growth (see Moustacchi and Williamson, 1966). A mechanism ensuring perpetuation of at least one MDNA template per cell must exist, since more or less all cells can regenerate mitochondria if transferred to conditions inducing respiration. This aspect is further discussed below in the case of the gi mutant.

Genetics of the respiratory system

A prerequisite for genetic analysis is a heritable mutational change. In the case of mitochondria, mutational changes have been detected mainly as deficiencies in the respiratory system, but only in microorganisms. This is because the technique of sampling and plating cells is available in this class of organisms and allows the detection of one mutant cell among a large number of normal ones. A method for sampling cells in tissues or in tissue cultures has not yet been developed. However, in view of the striking similarities in the general features of structure and function between mitochondria of widely different cell types, it is likely that the genetic findings in one case apply in large measure to the majority of cases.

Respiratory deficiency in yeast

The petite mutant. Ephrussi (1953) and his collaborators analysed a mutant of the yeast *Saccharomyces cerevisiae* which was unable to utilize non-fermentable substrates such as glycerol due to the absence of respiratory enzymes, cytochromes *a* and *b*, and certain dehydrogenases. On a solid medium containing a fermentable sugar, the mutant produces colonies that are small compared with the normal, hence the name 'petite' used by Ephrussi to designate this class of mutant. More detailed analysis of enzyme deficiencies in the petite mutant has been made by Sherman and Slonimski (1964). Their results were extended by Roodyn and Wilkie (1966) using a convenient automatic multiple-enzyme assay procedure (Table 2). The most striking changes in the mutant concerned the lactate dehydrogenase system in which a dramatic fall in L(+)-lactate dehydrogenase activity (measured as ferricyanide reductase) was consistently accompanied by a rise in the corresponding D(−)-lactate-ferricyanide reductase. This finding applied to a number of different petite strains. Other features noted in the early studies include the relatively high rate of mutation to petite of about 10^{-2} to 10^{-3} and the remarkable stability of the mutation. Indeed, the apparent irreversible nature of the mutant change has led to the hypothesis that the change is

TABLE 2 Ferricyanide reductases of normal and cytoplasmic petite strains of *Saccharomyces cerevisiae*

Strain	Ferricyanide reductase ($\mu moles/min/mg$ of protein N)			
	NADH-	L(+)-Lactate-	D(−)-Lactate-	Succinate-
A: normal strains				
4Cl	2·64	2·09	0·02	0·01
10	4·81	0·97	0	0·10
21	4·20	0·60	0	0·06
40	0·95	0·17	0·33	0·01
45	2·96	1·40	0·10	0·15
188	1·80	0·35	0·38	0·01
X1 (diploid)	2·90	1·78	0·01	0·06
40 × 41 (diploid)	3·92	1·74	0·01	0·15
Average	3·02	1·14	0·11	0·07
B: cytoplasmic petite strains				
45 sp	2·42	0·15	0·80	0·02
45 ac	2·03	0·03	0·73	0
4Cl sp	1·30	0·09	0·13	0
4Cl sp/Co	1·42	0·01	0·39	0
188 uv	0·94	0	0·60	0
45 ac × 188 uv (diploid)	1·57	0·04	0·52	0
45 sp × 4Cl sp (diploid)	1·00	0	0·22	0
Average	1·53	0·05	0·48	0·003
$\dfrac{\text{Average B}}{\text{Average A}} \times 100$	51	4·4	436	4·2

due to a loss rather than a structural alteration in a genetic factor. That this factor has a cytoplasmic location was evident from its non-Mendelian behaviour in crosses between petites and normals in which the mutant character failed to appear among the sexual progeny (Fig. 13). Chromosomal genes show Mendelian inheritance with mutant and normal progeny segregating in strict and predictable ratios. The generally accepted interpretation of these findings is that in the diploid cells resulting from fusion of petite and normal haploid cells, the intact cytoplasmic genetic factor is reintroduced by the normal parent strain. The factor, generally referred to as the rho (ρ) particle (Sherman, 1964), can then replicate and be transmitted to all diploid daughter cells during vegetative growth and to all ascospores following meiotic division. Cells failing to inherit the particle would be petite or rho minus (ρ^-) according to the scheme. The term 'neutral petite' is applied to those petite strains that conform to this pattern.

When any two ρ^- strains of independent origin are crossed, the resulting diploid cells are also ρ^-, indicating that all of these cytoplasmic mutants result from the same basic mutational change, otherwise complementation with restoration of functional mitochondria might be expected. Failure to detect complementation or somatic recombination in many millions of diploid cells derived from crosses between different ρ^- strains both spontaneous and variously induced (Roodyn and Wilkie, 1966) supports this hypothesis.

Further genetic analysis of these crosses is not possible since diploid petite cells are unable to sporulate. The process of sporulation apparently requires a respiratory system. Yotsuyanagi (1962) has made an electron-microscope study of ρ^- cells and finds mitochondria are aberrant and lack an inner membrane. Thus there is a morphological correlation with the biochemical lesions in the petite mutant.

The suppressive petite

This simple scheme of a petite cell resulting from the failure to inherit functional rho factor with restoration of the normal unit in the diploid via the normal parental cell does not cover the case of suppressive petites. Ephrussi et al. (1955), investigating this class of petite, found that a proportion of the zygote cells from crosses to normal failed to transmit the rho factor to their diploid daughter cells during vegetative multiplication (Fig. 13). The proportion of zygotes showing this pattern of behaviour was found to be strain dependent and could be as high as 99 per cent.

These investigators further reported that petite cells derived from the ascospores possessed the property of suppressiveness, and that the

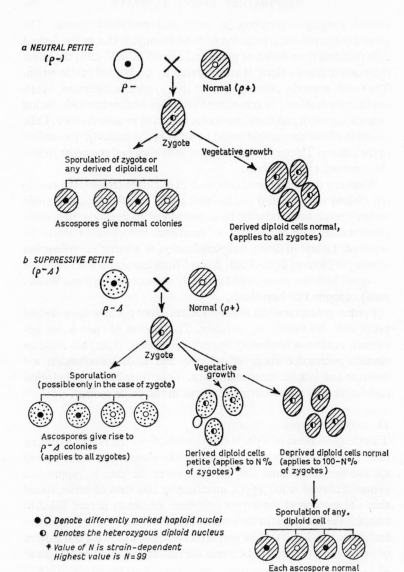

a NEUTRAL PETITE
(ρ−)

ρ− × Normal (ρ+)

↓

Zygote

Sporulation of zygote or any derived diploid cell

Ascospores give normal colonies

Vegetative growth

Derived diploid cells normal, (applies to all zygotes)

b SUPPRESSIVE PETITE
(ρ−Δ)

ρ−Δ × Normal (ρ+)

↓

Zygote

Sporulation (possible only in the case of zygote)

Ascospores give rise to ρ−Δ colonies (applies to all zygotes)

Vegetative growth

Derived diploid cells petite (applies to N% of zygotes) *

Deprived diploid cells normal (applies to 100−N% of zygotes)

Sporulation of any diploid cell

Each ascospore normal

● ○ Denote differently marked haploid nuclei

◑ Denotes the heterozygous diploid nucleus

* Value of N is strain-dependent
Highest value is N = 99

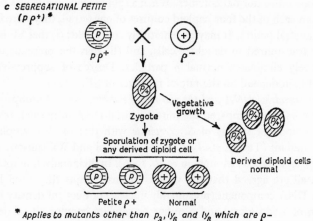

c SEGREGATIONAL PETITE
(ρ ρ⁺) *

pp⁺   ρ⁻

Zygote   Vegetative growth

Sporulation of zygote or
any derived diploid cell

Derived diploid cells
normal

Petite ρ +   Normal

* Applies to mutants other than p_3, ly_6 and ly_8 which are ρ−

FIG. 13 Petite inheritance in yeast

degree of suppressiveness generally could be lowered by the action of mutagens, although no details were given of the treatment in these cases.

Ephrussi and Grandchamp (1965) have subsequently shown that the degree of suppressiveness is a characteristic of each cell of the suppressive strain and is not a measure of the frequency of suppressive cells in a mixed population of neutral and suppressive petite cells. From a series of cloning experiments they found a strong correlation between parent-cell and daughter-cell lineages in their degree of suppressiveness. In a further paper Ephrussi et al. (1966) conclude that suppressiveness is under the control of a suppressive factor (SF) which acts conditionally to inhibit ρ particle replication (see also Wilkie, 1964).

Since the ascospores of suppressed zygotes give rise to suppressive petite colonies, it must be concluded that SF is transmitted through these ascospores to daughter cells in these cases. Results of an experiment in the author's laboratory (Wilkie, unpublished) provide evidence that SF is not transmitted by non-suppressed zygotes. In a cross between a suppressive petite and a normal, about 60 per cent of zygotes gave rise to petite colonies. Tetrad analysis of asci obtained from one of the normal colonies showed that all ascospores were normal and developed into normal colonies. When a spontaneous petite was picked up from each of the four haploid cultures of one tetrad, they were found to be neutral petites. It may be tentatively concluded: (i) that SF is passively transmitted to daughter cells, and (ii) that the presence of SF effectively eliminates normal ρ particles. Degree of suppressiveness would then depend on the rate of turnover of SF.

Mitochondrial DNA and the rho-minus mutant. Several groups of investigators have compared the mitochondrial DNA of normal, respiratory component strains of *S. cerevisiae* with that of the cytoplasmic petite mutant (Tewari *et al.*, 1966; Moustacchi and Williamson, 1966; Corneo *et al.*, 1966; Mounolou *et al.*, 1966). In their analysis of total cell DNA all are agreed that the various normal strains they used had a major DNA component (presumably nuclear) of buoyant density in the region of 1·700 g/cm³ and a minor or satellite component of density around 1·682 g/cm³ which could be concentrated in mitochondrial fractions. A second minor component of density higher than either of these two has also been described, but it is of unknown affinity.

Corneo *et al.*, and Moustacchi and Williamson report that the mitochondrial band is not detectable in whole cell DNA of various cytoplasmic (rho-minus) petite strains (Fig. 14), while Tewari *et al.* claim to detect very small amounts in mitochondrial fractions from their rho-minus strain. On the other hand, Mounolou *et al.* find DNA in their mitochondrial preparations of rho-minus petite but of higher buoyant density than that of a normal. In the neutral petite it is of density 1·687 g/cm³, while in a suppressive petite it is 1·695 g/cm³. Also the amounts of mitochondrial DNA of various buoyant densities appear to remain the same. The refinement introduced into these investigations by the last-named authors is that all strains used are derived from the same parental strain which has a gene-determined respiratory deficiency to begin with. Mounolou *et al.* conclude that the cytoplasmic petite mutation results from alteration, which may be gross, in the mitochondrial DNA. The result is apparently nonsense DNA which is incapable of reversion to normal. However, it is difficult to find a hypothesis to explain spontaneous change of this magnitude bearing in mind that it does not involve prior mutation of a nuclear gene: it would have to be self-inflicted, so to speak, or so it would appear. If the petite mitochondrial DNA is nonsensical, it may be deduced that the DNA polymerase which keeps it turning over is specified by genetic information other than that carried in mitochondrial DNA.

Whatever the mechanism of petite mutation, there is effective loss of the mitochondrial DNA. The tacit assumption is made here that this DNA is the rho factor, the normal function of which is to control the

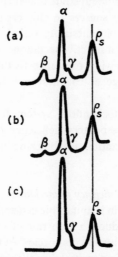

FIG. 14 Microdensitometer tracings from density-gradient preparations of yeast DNA. The peak on the right of each tracing is the reference DNA (*Pseudomonas*, density 1·727 g/cm³). α, β, and γ had densities of 1·699 g/cm³, 1·683 g/cm³, and 1·706 g/cm³ respectively

    (*a*) Strain 74, twenty-four hours culture
    (*b*) Strain 74, six hours culture
    (*c*) Strain 74A, a cytoplasmic petite mutant
      (After Moustacci and Williamson, 1966)

synthesis of the inner membrane system of the mitochondrion. That it carries the information for specifying all the proteins associated with the inner membrane, that is, membranous and enzymic, is a possibility and will be discussed later.

Further aspects of mutational change in the respiratory system of yeast

By limiting the energy source to non-fermentable substrates such as glycerol and lactate, it is possible to enforce the development and main-tenance of the respiratory system to the exclusion of the fermentation cycle in *S. cerevisiae*. Under these conditions the effects of specific in-hibitors of mitochondrial genesis can be clearly seen as inhibitors of growth. Specificity of action can be recognized by showing no inhibition of growth when fermentable substrate is available. This facility of mani-pulating the two energy sources in this organism is most useful in studies of mitochondrial biogenesis. As well as demonstrating inhibition of the system it provides a selective technique for the identification and isolation of mutants showing resistance to the inhibitors. In plating experiments these emerge as colonies on a background of inhibited cells.

Inhibitors of the mitochondrial system fall into two categories: (i) mutagens inducing respiratory deficiency particularly of the cyto-plasmic type, and (ii) antibiotics blocking protein synthesis in the organelle.

Induction of respiratory deficiency by acridines

The acridine dye acriflavin is mutagenic generally, but in concentrations as low as 1 p.p.m. it induces a high rate of mutation to ρ^- petite in growing cultures of Saccharomyces species. At these levels there is little or no apparent mutagenic activity other than petite induction, and cell viability is high. Ephrussi (1953), reviewing the pioneer work of his group in this field, describes experiments in which normal cells were observed under the microscope on a medium containing 3 μg/ml acriflavin. As daughter cells were budded off, they were removed by micromanipulation and analysed for respiratory ability. Almost 100 per cent of daughter cells were found to be ρ^- petite, but the parent cells retained the ability to respire and to give rise to normal buds when sub-sequently transferred to a medium without acriflavin. These results were interpreted to mean that acriflavin either blocks the replication of the ρ factor or interferes with the mechanism of its transmission. In either case, cells budded off fail to inherit functional mitochondrial DNA.

Acriflavin has been shown to bind to DNA *in vitro* and to become intercalated in the DNA double helix, resulting presumably in errors at replication *in vivo* (Lerman, 1963). Extensive intercalation could conceivably preclude replication of DNA or result in altered replicas along the lines described by Mounolou *et al.* However, Riva (1966) has found that non-mutagenic methylated acridines also bind strongly to DNA and show intercalation, suggesting that these reactions with DNA do not account entirely for the mutagenic effects of acriflavin. In view of the findings of Tewari *et al.* (1966), that there is preferential intercalation between acridines and the mitochondrial DNA as against the nuclear DNA of yeast, it would seem the *petite* mutation could result from this process. However, preferential intercalation would not explain fully the wide differences in mutagenic activity regarding the two types of DNA. From plating experiments on glycerol medium, it appears our strains are inhibited by amounts of the dye ranging from 0·1 to 0·5 μg/ml. That is, there is 100 per cent induction of *petite* among daughter cells initially budded off, leading to failure to develop visible colonies. No other mutagenic effect of the acriflavine at these concentrations is apparent, such as forward mutation to cycloheximide resistance and adenine deficiency, or back mutation to uracil and histidine independence. The differential mutagenic effect of the dye on the respiratory determinant is emphasized by the fact that the induced petite cells will grow in a medium containing between 200 and 500 μg/ml (depending on the strain), so long as fermentable substrate is available.

Spontaneous mutants of *S. cerevisiae* showing resistance to acriflavine ranging from 1 to 20 μg/ml have been isolated from glycerol-dye plates (Thomas and Wilkie, 1967). That this is resistance of the mitochondrial system to mutagenic action, and not a mutational change leading to alteration in permeability of the cell to the dye or to a mechanism for inactivating the mutagen, can be shown by demonstrating that there is no concomitant decrease in the inhibitory effects of the dye on sugar-dye medium. In one particular case a fifty-fold increase in resistance to induction of respiratory deficiency has been accompanied by an actual two-fold increase in sensitivity to acriflavine on a sugar-containing medium. Further evidence that we are dealing with the desired type of mutant has come from the study of mitochondrial fractions from cells treated with acriflavine and which show the fluorescence associated with the presence of the dye. Genetic analysis of a few such mutants indicates that recessive nuclear genes control the resistance, and so far cytoplasmic inheritance of resistance which would reflect a direct heritable change in the mitochondrial DNA itself has not been observed. This is in general agreement with the fact that spontaneous mutation rate to resistance is of the order of 10^{-5} (gene frequency), and UV-induction also follows the same pattern as for gene mutation. It is possible these genes are involved in making specific polymerases for mitochondrial DNA and RNA, and that these enzymes are distinct from nuclear polymerases. The inhibitory effect of the dye on respiratory enzyme synthesis (Slonimski, 1953) could be due to interference with the function of the RNA polymerase (Richardson, 1966), while the mutagenic effect could result from similar activity in the case of DNA polymerase. It could be argued that mutation of these genes results in mutant but functional polymerases which have a reduced affinity for the mutagen. This would show up as resistance to the dye. Binding of acridine to DNA may be a factor, in which case the degree of intercalation could determine resistance levels. These hypotheses are open to experimental test.

In *Saccharomyces cerevisiae* acriflavin inhibits the synthesis of respiratory enzymes in cells adapting to aerobic conditions (Slonimski, 1953). It is likely that one stage in the reaction caused by the dye is common to both inhibition and mutagenesis, but it is unlikely that the inhibition results in the petite mutation: repression of cytochromes (e.g. by anaerobiosis) in itself does not cause petite formation except in a special case described below.

Bulder (1964) has looked in more detail at acriflavin action in a wide variety of yeast species and finds that whereas all species of Saccharomyces (*in sensu stricto*) are induced to form petites by the dye ('petite positive'), most other species are 'petite negative' and do not give rise to petites (see also De Deken, 1961). Although there is this clear division into two groups regarding petite induction, the synthesis of respiratory enzymes is inhibited by acriflavin in both groups to the same extent. Bulder concludes from these results that the primary action of the dye is the same in all yeasts, namely, inhibition of respiratory enzymes, and implies that in the petite-positive yeasts this leads to the mutational event, but in petite-negative species there is a stage at which the mutation fails to express itself. An alternative explanation is that acriflavin action is two-fold: (i) it can repress genetic information for cytochrome synthesis; (ii) it can act as a mutagen and specifically knock out the

ρ particle. Whether the second feature is seen could depend on the availability of the ρ particle to acriflavin action.

The presence of two sites sensitive to acriflavin in the mitochondrial determinant (mitochondrial DNA), one for repression of respiratory enzymes and one for duplication, is discussed by De Deken (1966), but he expresses a preference for a model with only one site sensitive to the dye. In petite positives, binding to this site is considered to lead simultaneously to loss of phenotypic expression and loss of ability to duplicate, while in petite-negative strains only the former effect is seen. However, it is easier (if easy is the right word) to visualize loss of regulation at the duplication site, giving insensitivity to repressive action by the dye, in the two-site model, than loss of one function at a single site which is bi-functional. Loss of repressibility in the two-site model would, of course, lead to the petite-negative situation.

In the same report De Deken finds a correlation between the manifestation of the crabtree effect and the ability to give rise to petites. All petite-positive yeasts show glucose repression of the respiratory enzymes, while petite-negative species do not, with the exception of two cases. There is a correlation, then, between repressibility of the respiratory system and its genetic instability.

The gi mutant of S. cerevisiae. The connexion between repression and mutation is brought into sharp focus in a mutant yeast which shows induction of respiratory deficiency by glucose (g*i*) (Wilkie and Negrotti, 1967). The cells of this strain of *S. cerevisiae* grow well on non-fermentable substrates and have a normal complement of cytochromes when scanned in the recording spectrophotometer. However, this manifestation of respiratory competence is seen only under conditions inducing respiration, that is, in the presence of oxygen and with energy sources other than glucose. Under conditions of glucose repression or anoxia the daughter cells budded off are cytoplasmic petites, although the parent cell remains respiratory competent and will bud off normal cells once more if removed to a non-repressing medium. These points were established by micromanipulation techniques in the study of cell lineages. When g*i* cells, which are routinely maintained and subcultured on a glycerol-containing medium, are inoculated into a liquid glucose–yeast extract medium in shaking culture, the ratio of petite to g*i* cells (respiratory competent) increases exponentially with time to a maximum, during which the total number of g*i* cells remains more or less the same. This is followed by the reverse process when respiratory competent cells increase in number relative to the respiratory deficient ones which have stopped dividing. The changeover occurs about the time when glucose has been depleted from the medium. If anaerobic conditions are applied, petite cells only are produced and this occurs in the presence of non-repressing sugars such as galactose.

The phenotypic expression of the g*i* mutant is most striking when cells are plated on glucose–agar medium. The initial cells of the developing colony are petite and give a flat base to the colony from which a papilla of g*i* cells erupts subsequently. The extent of the petite base is proportional to the amount of glucose in the medium.

The conclusion drawn from these findings is that continuity of the rho factor is possible in the g*i* strain only by way of intact, functional mitochondria. When the organelle disintegrates under repression, the mechanism of replication and/or transmission which normally comes into play at this time is not functional in this mutant – that there are two distinct mechanisms for perpetuating the mitochondrial information, one for repression and the other for induction, is evident from these findings in the g*i* mutant. Genetic analysis has shown the g*i* character to be under the control of a recessive nuclear gene, so it can be said that this gene normally functions in ensuring the continuity of mitochondrial DNA when the respiratory system is repressed. It could be argued that all mitochondrial DNA becomes ineffective as replicating units under repression, and that a new system involving both a master copy of the mitochondrial DNA, which would survive organelle disintegration, and the g*i* gene comes into operation. The hypothesis of a master template emerged from the results of UV-induction of petite in which anaerobic cells showed a linear relationship (single-hit effect) between dose and mutation, whereas aerobic cells showed multiple-hit induction curves (Wilkie, 1963).

Nuclear genes and the respiratory system in yeast

The p series of genes. A number of respiratory mutants unable to utilize non-fermentable substrates as an energy source and which are gene-determined have been isolated following the original discovery of a 'segregational' petite by Ephrussi (1953). This category of mutant is recognized by a two to two segregation of respiratory deficiency to normal in ascospore tetrads from crosses to normal. These gene petites (the p series) fall into one or other of two classes depending on the respiratory capacity of the diploids in crosses to the neutral ρ^- petite. In those cases where complementation is seen, that is, where the diploids are respiratory competent, it may be concluded these gene mutants are ρ^+ with respect to the cytoplasmic factor (Fig. 13). Where there is no complementation with the ρ^- strain, the segregational mutants in this case may be assumed to be ρ^-. Of nine mutants of the p series analysed by Sherman (1963), and Sherman and Slonimski (1964), the strains carrying the mutant genes p_3, ly_6, and ly_8 respectively, showed no complementation with the cytoplasmic petite and were designated ρ^-. As expected, pairwise crossing of these p gene mutants *inter se* produced respiratory-deficient diploids, since ρ^- strains do not complement each other. The strains carrying ly_6 and ly_8 as well as being ρ^- have a simultaneous requirement for lysine leading to the conclusion that the loss of the ρ particle in some way results from a lesion in the lysine biosynthetic pathway in these cells. The ly_6 and ly_8 mutations apparently cause lesions at different points in this pathway, since the doubly heterozygous diploid $ly_{6/+}$ $ly_{8/+}$ obtained by crossing ly_6 and ly_8 does not require lysine. It is nevertheless respiratory deficient – the cytoplasmic determinant once having been lost cannot be regenerated. Genetic analysis of a revertant to lysine independence in the ly_8 strain provides good evidence that the lysine requirement and respiratory deficiency are effects of a single gene change.

The main point to be taken from these studies with non-complementing segregational mutants is that there appear to be nuclear genes controlling the replication, and hence the transmission of the cytoplasmic determinant.

Gene changes resulting in a high rate of production of cells during vegetative growth (Ephrussi and Hottinguer, 1951; Horn, 1965) probably also come into this category of regulating the replication of the ρ particle.

The six remaining mutants investigated, namely, p_1, p_2, p_4, p_5, p_6, and p_7, all complemented the ρ^- strain and were assumed to be ρ^+. Sherman and Slonimski (1964) also investigated the extent of the lesions in the respiratory system and found this varied with the particular mutant

G

gene carried. For example, p_4 strains were actually capable of respiring although ineffectually, due to low concentrations of cytochromes $a + a_3$ and b. p_5 strains had no apparent cytochromes $a + a_3$, while p_1, p_6, and p_7 strains all resembled the ρ^- petite in lacking cytochromes $a + a_3$ and b. All ρ^- strains irrespective of p genes carried in the nucleus showed the same multiple deficiencies characteristic of the cytoplasmic mutant. It was pointed out that none of the genes can be regarded as controlling induction of cytochromes since no mutant strain lacks all normal cytochromes, as in wholly repressed cells under anoxia, for example. However, mutation at any one of these p loci leads to multiple enzyme deficiencies.

An interesting observation of Yotsuyanagi (1962) in electron-microscope studies of various respiratory mutants is that morphologically aberrant mitochondria were clearly seen only in ρ^- petite strains. Strains carrying p-gene mutations had apparently normal mitochondria, with the possible exception of p_6, although some of these strains had the petite phenotype. From these findings it would appear that the inner membrane of the organelle can be formed, at least to some extent, without concomitant synthesis of cytochromes a, a_3, and b.

Jakob (1965) has made a detailed analysis of the kinetics of complementation with a neutral ρ^- strain in the case of the p_1, p_5, and p_7 mutants. Using a highly sensitive system for detecting oxygen uptake, she was able to make direct measurements of the onset of respiration in zygotes immediately after their formation and through several generations of vegetative multiplication. In each of the crosses between the respective gene mutant and the ρ^- strain, all zygotes showed a lag in the development of respiratory activity. This lag period differed characteristically for each gene, and was 0·5, 4·8, and 9·7 hours for p_5, p_7, and p_1 respectively. In crosses *inter se* giving zygotes of genotypes $p_{1/+} p_{5/+}$, $p_{1/+} p_{7/+}$, and $p_{5/+} p_{7/+}$ the lag was 0·5, 4·8, and 0·5 respectively. In other words, the duration of the lag period corresponded to that of the mutant with the shorter adaptation time. From these findings it would appear that complementation is not simply de-repression of a previously repressed genome, but that the expression of genetic information in elaborating the respiratory system is a secondary effect of the restoration of functional alleles of the p genes. Jakob favours the theory that the primary effect of the mutations is to alter mitochondrial structure in such a way as to block the synthesis or the function of one of the components of the electron transport system. Put another way, the complementing genes could be said to function in making structural protein units which are assembled following a time sequence. When put together the structure forms the base for insertion of the specific proteins.

In analogy with an automobile, the structural protein can be regarded as the housing for the power unit; if not properly constructed, the unit either cannot be put in, or if it is put in it cannot be properly connected up to the crankshaft.

Jakob further reports that in all zygotes studied, oxygen uptake is extremely high as soon as respiration is initiated. This is followed by a reduced rate of O_2 uptake giving a clear indication of regulation of the respiratory system following an initial de-repression phase.

The cy mutants of Saccharomyces cerevisiae

Sherman (1964) and collaborators have developed techniques for isolating mutants that are deficient in cytochrome c (cy mutants) but have approximately normal amounts of other cytochromes. Analysis of these mutants indicate so far that there are six unlinked genes, cy_1 to cy_6, controlling cytochrome c synthesis. More specifically, mutations of the cy_1 gene block iso-1-cytochrome c synthesis, while mutants at the other five loci have both iso-1- and iso-2-cytochrome c, but in decreased amounts. Furthermore, mutations at different sites within the same locus lead to differences in the utilization of non-fermentable carbon sources. For example, cy_{3-1}, cy_{3-3}, cy_{3-5}, and cy_{3-6} are all mutants of the cy_3 gene, but cy_{3-1} and cy_{3-3} do not require a fermentable substrate while the others do. Again some cy mutants have a limited ability to utilize non-fermentable substrates and have a marked decrease in growth rate in media with these substrates as energy sources.

Using sophisticated techniques for the analysis of intact proteins and haem peptides in strain cy_{1-2} and its revertant CY_{1-2}, Sherman et al. (1966) have shown that the CY_1 gene codes for the primary structure of iso-1-cytochrome c. In other words, cytochrome c synthesis proceeds through the microsomal system in the usual way for constitutive enzymes and is not dependent on mitochondrial genetic information. On the other hand, it appears that cytochrome a synthesis is regulated by cytochrome c from the work of Ycas (1956), and Reilly and Sherman

(1965). For example, Ycas showed that when baker's yeast is cultured in the presence of antimycin A, which specifically blocks electron transport, synthesis of a is inhibited while there is no effect on b and c. Also in the cy mutants requiring a fermentable substrate and in which cytochrome c content was low, cytochrome a synthesis was very sensitive to glucose repression. The precise connexion between cytochrome c synthesis and the repressive action of glucose is not known.

Sherman and Slonimski (1964) looked at the cytochrome pattern of strains carrying various combinations of P and CY mutations with and without the ρ factor. In general, all ρ^- strains, regardless of their P and CY complement, showed the same pattern having no $a + a_3$ or b, and high levels of c. However, interaction of P and CY genes is indicated from the cytochromes of ρ^+ cells of genotype $p_7\ cy_1$, where cytochrome levels are higher than in the corresponding $p_7\ CY\ \rho^+$ and $P\ cy_1\ \rho^+$ strains. It is concluded that the mutant gene p_7 partially suppresses the mutant effect of cy_1 and vice versa.

These studies with respiratory-deficient mutants give some measure of the complexity of the genetic control of the biosynthesis of the cytochromes involving nuclear genes and cytoplasmic genetic information. It seems that nuclear genes are involved in making mitochondrial enzymes, and also in the control of both the replication and functional state of the mitochondrial DNA.

CHAPTER SEVEN

Respiratory System of Neurospora

Respiratory deficiency in Neurospora

The experiments of Luck described in Chapter Two provide good evidence that the mitochondria of the filamentous fungus *Neurospora crassa* are perpetuated by division of pre-existing mitochondria during vegetative growth. From the knowledge accumulated so far on mitochondrial genesis, it may be assumed at the outset that the synthesis (growth) of the organelle in *Neurospora* depends on genetic information both in nuclear and mitochondrial DNA. Respiratory deficiency arising by mutational change in the former would show Mendelian inheritance in sexual progeny, while mutations in the latter would be non-Mendelian or cytoplasmic in their pattern of inheritance. Both classes of respiratory mutant have been found in this organism, and some points of similarity with the yeast system can be seen.

Cytoplasmic respiratory mutants. In sexual reproduction fertilization is effected by seeding of protoperithecia (the female sexual organ) with asexual, vegetative spores (conidia) of opposite mating type. The protoperithecium is a comparatively large structure with a receptive protuberance called the trichogyne, and an analogy with a sperm and egg system can be drawn. The conidium apparently contributes only a nucleus at fertilization so that cytoplasmic factors are maternally inherited (for a review of maternal inheritance see Wilkie, 1964). After fertilization, the meiotic products, the ascospores, are formed.

Several maternally inherited (*mi*) respiratory deficiencies have been analysed by Mitchell and Mitchell (1952) and a diagram of inheritance patterns is shown in Fig. 15. The *mi* mutants considered here, namely *mi-1* (poky), *mi-3*, and *mi-4*, are phenotypically distinguishable. *mi-1* is deficient in cytochromes *a* and *b* but produces larger than normal amounts of cytochrome *c*. *mi-3* differs from *mi-1* in showing the presence

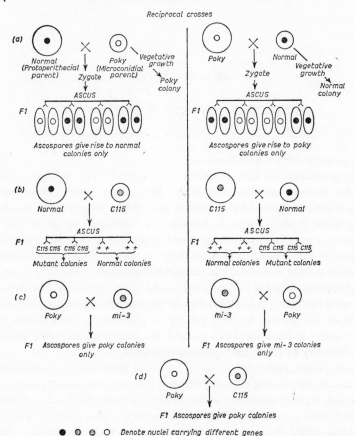

● ⦿ ⊖ ○ Denote nuclei carrying different genes

FIG. 15 Inheritance of respiratory deficiency in *Neurospora*

of cytochrome *b* and less of *c*, while *mi-4*, although having the same cytochrome lesions as *mi-1*, can be cultured on a sorbose medium. In reciprocal crosses between *mi-1* and *mi-3* or *mi-4* (Pittinger, 1956), the mitochondrial type again follows that of the protoperithecial parent.

It is important to note that conidia possess mitochondrial genetic information, and when used as vegetative propagants germinate and produce mycelia with the mitochondrial type of the parent strain. It appears, then, that this information is rejected at fertilization and that maternal mitochondria are selected and transmitted to the ascospores. Reich and Luck (1966) have looked at this aspect of mitochondrial inheritance in terms of mitochondrial DNA, having previously found that the cross-compatible species *N. crassa* and *N. sitophila* differ in their mitochondrial DNA complement. Mitochondrial DNA of *N. crassa* contains two DNA populations with buoyant densities in CsCl corresponding to 1·698 and 1·702 respectively. The mitochondria of *N. sitophila*, in addition to DNA species of these densities, have a unique major DNA component banding at 1·692. A cross between an *mi-1* strain of *N. crassa*, mitochondrial DNA's of which showed no detectable differences in density from normal *N. crassa* strains (i.e. DNA 1·698 × 1·702), and a respiratory competent strain of *N. sitophila* with the DNA 1·692 component was analysed. With the *N. crassa* as maternal parent, all ascospore progeny were of the *mi-1* type as expected, and none of these contained DNA 1·692. In another series of crosses the inheritance of DNA 1·692 through the maternal parent was likewise established. Thus a clear correlation between the inheritance of mitochondrial type and that of mitochondrial DNA was observed.

The integrity of individual mitochondrial forms in mixed populations of mitochondria has been established by studies with heterokaryons. Heterokaryons result from hyphal fusions between different strains and are comprised of mixed populations of respective nuclei and cytoplasmic inclusions in a common cytoplasmic matrix. For example, sectors of *mi-1* and *mi-3* have been observed to segregate out of heterokaryotic mycelia of the two mutants. An important observation was the finding of physiological complementation between *mi-1* and *mi-4* since their heterokaryon had normal growth. It is difficult to visualize interaction between two differently deficient mitochondria to produce a normal end product. There was no complementation at the genetic level, that is, no normal mitochondria were made as far as could be determined (Pittinger, 1956). More recently elegant experiments of interhyphal transplantation have demonstrated the genetic continuity of mitochondrial characters (Diacumakos, Garnjobst, and Tatum, 1965). These authors extracted mitochondria from a cytoplasmic mutant, *abn-1*, similar in most respects to *mi-1*, and injected them into hyphal cells of a normal strain. It was found that many of the features of the *abn-1* mutation appeared after a time lapse in the new mycelium.

However, the cytochrome lesions were not exactly the same as *abn*-1, so that a simple explanation of differential survival of *abn*-1 mitochondria over normal was not acceptable, and possible interaction of normal and abnormal mitochondria on regulatory processes was considered. The abnormalities were maternally inherited, clearly demonstrating the continuity of mitochondrial type.

The nature of the biochemical lesions in the *mi*-1 and *mi*-3 mutants was investigated by Woodward and Munkres (1966). From amino-acid analysis of purified mitochondrial structural protein (MSP) they found that the MSP of *mi*-1 has one less tryptophan residue per mole of MSP and one more cisteine residue than MSP of normal, wild-type strains. In the case of *mi*-3, only the tryptophan deficiency is apparent in the amino-acid composition of MSP. They conclude that the *mi*-1 and *mi*-3 mutations most probably result from alterations in MDNA, which result in single amino-acid replacement. Changes of this kind would be analogous to point mutations in nuclear genes specifying proteins, and of course would not be detectable as alterations in buoyant density of DNA.

The fundamental point is that amino-acid replacement in apparently one protein results in multiple enzyme deficiency. This reflects the interdependence of the various proteins of the membrane assembly.

Munkres and Woodward (1966) go on to stress the importance of stereospecificity of enzymes and structural protein in determining the functional properties of the mitochondrial complex. Results of inter-actions between purified malate dehydrogenase from malate gene mutants and normal strains, and purified structural elements of mito-chondria, lead to the conclusion that phenotypic effects can be brought about by genetic alteration of 'location specificity' of the enzyme. The corollary may also apply that alteration in MSP leads to misplacement of enzyme(s) with a consequent effect on enzyme(s) function. Other aspects of these investigations of Munkres and Woodward are dis-cussed in Chapter Three.

Gene-determined respiratory deficiency. Two respiratory mutants, C 115 and C 117, have been shown to be gene-determined and to act independently of the *mi* mutations (Mitchell and Mitchell, 1956), since each of these mutational changes has recognizable differences in cyto-chrome lesions. C 115 has no cytochrome *a*, a small amount of *c* but significantly more b than wild-type, while C 117 has no detectable a or c, but again more b than wild-type. It is clear there is a complexity of nuclear and cytoplasmic interactions in determining the final arrangement of respiratory enzymes in the mitochondrion, and a qualitative alteration in any one component may have profound effects on other parts of the system both qualitative and quantitative. For example, strain C 117 may be a cytochrome c mutant comparable to the cy mutants in yeast, and this lesion results in failure of functional a to appear. This in turn may have resulted in a breakdown in the regulation of b production which is built into the system in excess amounts.

The inferred point mutations in mitochondrial DNA affect the system at the architectural level apparently. Such point mutations seem to occur with the same frequency as nuclear gene mutations judging by the rarity of mi mutants. As far as the authors are aware, the individual mi mutants are unique in *Neurospora*, and nothing comparable to the genetic instability of the mitochondrion of the petite yeasts is seen. This is probably due to the fact that *Neurospora* is an obligate aerobe and does not have a mechanism for repression of the respiratory system with which the petite mutation is associated. The general metabolism of the obligate aerobe is closely geared to a mitochondrion with a stable organization.

A point of interest is that the apparent complete lack of cytochromes a, a_3, and b in mi-1, for example, does not stop growth although growth rate is much reduced. Presumably an alternative respiratory pathway is available in this fungus although of limited efficiency.

This account of respiratory deficiency in *Neurospora* is by no means exhaustive and the reader is referred to Wagner and Mitchell (1964), and Silagi (1965) for more detailed accounts of mutants.

CHAPTER EIGHT

Effects of Antibiotics on Mitochondrial Synthesis

Antibacterial antibiotics

The inhibition of amino-acid incorporation into mitochondrial protein *in vitro* by the antibacterial antibiotic chloramphenicol has already been described (Chapter Three). Reports in the literature of this effect are brief and the mechanism of the drug's activity in the *in vitro* system does not appear to have been followed up by the original investigators. Linnane and his co-workers subsequently demonstrated the inhibition of cytochrome *a* and *b* synthesis by the antibiotic in the intact cells of a diploid strain of *Saccharomyces cerevisiae* (Huang *et al.*, 1966; Clark-Walker and Linnane, 1966). Similar results were obtained with other antibacterial drugs, such as tetracycline and erythromycin, the common feature of which is the inhibition by these antibiotics of protein synthesis in bacteria (Clark-Walker and Linnane, 1966) (Fig. 16). The inhibitory effects on mitochondrial synthesis are reversible, and cells can proceed to make functional organelle when removed to a medium free of antibiotic provided fermentable substrate is available at least for the first few cell generations: turnover of the mitochondrial system is apparently necessary to dilute out the drug before synthesis of cytochromes can proceed. It was also established that the yeast cells grown in the presence of chloramphenicol have mitochondrial profiles (outer membrane), but no inner membrane when viewed in the electron microscope. This is in accordance with the fact that chloramphenicol does not inhibit the synthesis of cytochrome *c*. Linnane has put forward the hypothesis that chloramphenicol acts specifically to block translation of mitochondrial genetic information into protein of the inner membrane. Striking corroborative evidence in support of this is provided by a study of the effect of chloramphenicol on the *gi* mutant, in which, it may be remembered, repression of the respiratory system induces petiteness. Cells of the *gi* mutant are inhibited at a concentration of 0·2 mg/ml chloramphenicol on a medium with glycerol as the energy source (see below). At a concentration of 2 mg/ml with the non-repressing sugar galactose as substrate, there was no induction of petite among daughter

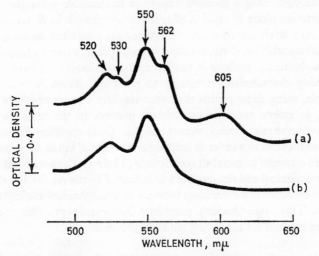

FIG. 16 Absorption spectra of a yeast strain sensitive to erythromycin
(*a*) Stationary-phase cells from a glucose-YEP culture
(*b*) Stationary-phase cells from a glucose-YEP culture which contains 100 g/ml erythromycin
Peaks at 605, 562, and 550 mμ in the α-region indicate cytochromes *a*, *b*, *c* + *c*$_1$ respectively, in the β-region, 530 and 520 mμ indicate cytochromes *b* and *c* respectively.

cells during growth of the culture, although it was established that cytochromes *a* and *b* were not being synthesized (Negrotti and Wilkie, 1967). It may be concluded that the informational complement of the mitochondrion is being maintained and transmitted in the presence of chloramphenicol and that the drug acts only at the time of translation of genetic information. This information could be encoded in the mito-chondrial DNA or could be coming in as messenger RNA from the nucleus.

The extension of these investigations to a number of haploid strains of yeast has shown that the level of tolerance to the inhibitory effects described is strain dependent, that is to say, resistance to the antibiotic in question has a genetic basis (Wilkie et al., 1967). The specificity of action of these antibacterial drugs on the respiratory system is emphasized by the fact that no inhibition of growth is detectable in a medium containing a plentiful supply of fermentable substrate since fermentation alone is capable of maintaining growth in S. cerevisiae. Resistance levels are therefore determined on a medium containing a non-fermentable substrate, usually glycerol, as energy source. Inhibition of mitochondrial synthesis in the latter situation inhibits growth.

Having characterized strains as to resistance levels, it was then possible, using those strains that were sensitive to comparatively low levels, to isolate spontaneous resistant mutants in the same way as acriflavin-resistant strains were obtained. Cross-checking resistance levels of mutants to a series of antibiotics was carried out in a number of cases in attempts to establish correlations (Table 3). Cross-resistance to chloramphenicol and tetracycline was indicated by the results, but there was no evidence of a correlation between chloramphenicol and erythromycin. This cross-checking procedure incidentally provides a convenient method for classifying antibacterial antibiotics.

Genetics of resistance to chloramphenicol and erythromycin
Genetic analysis of resistance of the respiratory system to chloramphenicol and erythromycin has been carried out in crosses between resistant mutants and sensitive strains in each case (Wilkie et al., 1967). To date, two dominant nuclear genes and one recessive gene have been identified conferring resistance to 1, 1·5, and 0·5 mg/ml chloramphenicol respectively, while in the case of erythromycin resistance a recessive gene has been recognized for resistance to 1 mg/ml. Cytoplasmic inheritance of erythromycin resistance has also been established in two cases (Thomas and Wilkie, 1968) and will be discussed in detail below. In a cross between a chloramphenicol-resistant strain and one resistant to erythromycin, independent assortment of the genes concerned was established, and no interaction was apparent in the double-resistant recombinant strain. This last finding further testified to the independent action of the two antibiotics.

Evidence of cytoplasmic control of resistance to erythromycin was

TABLE 3   Resistance levels of yeast strains to various antibiotics and of spontaneous resistant mutants of these strains

Strain	Resistance (mg/ml)*						
	CAP	TC	ER	CA	OL	SP	LI
22-4B	<0·1	0·1	<0·1	<0·5	2	5	10
22-4B-CAPR	1	1	<0·1	<0·5	2	5	10
41	0·1	0·1	0·1	0·5	10	2	10
41-CAPR	2	1	0·1	0·5	10	2	10
41-ERR	0·1	0·1	8	0·5	10	2	10
D243-P1	1	0·5	0·1	<0·5	5	<2	2
D243-P1-ERR	1	0·5	8	0·5	20	2	10
D243-F2	<0·1	0·25	0·1	<0·5	0·5	<2	<2
D243-F2-ERR	1	1	8	<0·5	0·5	2	10
10-19B	1	4	0·5	<0·5	5	<2	10
10,19B-ERR	1	4	8	0·5	10	2	10
10 (diploid)	2	0·5	0·1	<0·5	2	<2	10
10-ERR	2	1	8	0·5	5	2	10
M (diploid)	1	0·5	0·1	0·5	5	10	10
M-CAPR	4	2	0·1	0·5	5	10	10
4C1	0·5	0·5	0·5	<0·5	5	2	5
4C1-TCR	1	2	0·5	<0·5	5	2	5

Abbreviations: CA, carbomycin; OL, oleandomycin; SP, spiramycin. CAPR, ERR, and TCR denote spontaneous resistant mutants to chloramphenicol, erythromycin, and tetracycline respectively.

* Range of concentrations used (mg/ml): CAP, 0·1–4; TC, 0·1–4; ER, 0·1–8; CA, 0·5; OL, 0·5–20; SP, 2–10; LI, 2–10.

(From Wilkie *et al.*, 1967)

first provided by the results of a cross between a spontaneous mutant resistant to 5 mg/ml (isolated from a parent strain sensitive to 0·01 mg/ml) and a sensitive strain inhibited by 0·01 mg/ml of the drug. The cross was carried out on solid, glucose medium, and a number of diploid colonies that developed from individual zygotes were tested for resistance level by sampling and plating cells. Although all zygotes and their vegetative progeny were identical in nuclear genotype, it was found that individual samples, which numbered about 400 cells, varied in the proportion of cells resistant to erythromycin. The range was between 0 per cent and 100 per cent and all resistant cells were able to grow on

5 mg/ml, while sensitive cells were inhibited at 10 μg/ml, or in other words, no intermediate levels of resistance were seen. Sporulation of one of the diploids that was wholly sensitive according to the sampling test gave ascospore tetrads that all segregated 4:0 sensitive to resistant. Also about 400 random ascospores were found to be sensitive when tested in plating experiments. On the other hand, one of the diploids which had about 50 per cent of cells resistant when sporulated gave tetrads which ranged from 4:0 or 0:4 sensitive to resistant.

When zygotes were micromanipulated on to solid glycerol medium which had erythromycin added, it was found that each resulting diploid colony was comprised of 100 per cent resistant cells. All zygotes were able to give rise to colonies on the drug and spore tetrads all segregated 4:0 resistant to sensitive.

In all ascospore tests in the above series nuclear marker genes segregated in the expected Mendelian ratios.

These results gave a clear indication of cytoplasmic inheritance of resistance and allowed the working hypothesis to be made that mutation to resistance had taken place in the mitochondrial DNA. It could then be reasoned that fusion of resistant and sensitive cells gave zygotes with a complement of mixed mitochondrial types. Random distribution of mitochondria to daughter cells during vegetative growth could explain the apparent Poisson distribution of resistant cells in resulting colonies on non-selective medium. On a selective medium containing erythromycin, only mitochondria of resistant type would be perpetuated and transmitted. Likewise the mitochondrial type of sexual progeny (the ascospores) would be determined by the mitochondrial complement of the parental diploid cell.

The hypothesis of mutant mitochondrial DNA controlling resistance but being otherwise normal was tested by making use of the fact that the petite mutation effectively destroys mitochondrial DNA. The procedure was to isolate the cytoplasmic petite from both the resistant strain and the sensitive one following acriflavin treatment. Designating these $R\rho^-$ and $S\rho^-$ respectively, the crosses $R\rho^- \times S\rho^+$ and $R\rho^+ \times S\rho^-$ were set up. In the first cross all zygotes micromanipulated gave rise to colonies comprised wholly of sensitive cells on glycerol medium without erythromycin. On glycerol medium with drug added, zygotes were unable to produce colonies. Ascospore tetrads all segregated 4:0 sensitive to resistant. The conclusion was that the effective loss of mitochondrial DNA brought about by petite mutation produced a simultaneous loss of the resistance factor.

In the second cross all diploid colonies from zygotes were wholly resistant both on selective and non-selective media and ascospore tetrads all segregated 0:4 sensitive to resistant.

These results are believed to provide conclusive evidence that resistance to the inhibitory effects of erythromycin on mitochondrial synthesis can come about by a heritable change in mitochondrial DNA. This DNA is otherwise perfectly functional as has been seen by its behaviour in competition with non-mutant DNA and also from a study of the cytochrome spectrum of the resistant strain, in which a normal complement of these enzymes was observed: there was no detectable difference between this spectrum and that of the sensitive parent strain from which it was isolated.

An identical series of experiments was carried out on a second spontaneous resistant mutant isolated from a different sensitive strain from that mentioned above. In this case resistance level of the mutant was 3 mg/ml, while the parental strain was sensitive once more to 0·01 mg/ml.

Similar results to those in the first series were obtained. It has yet to be determined that different mutant sites are involved in the two cases.

This technique of using the cytoplasmic petite has an obvious general application to cases where mitochondrial mutation is suspected, and is being exploited in similar experiments with aminoglycosides resistance. The finding of a number of mitochondrial mutants would open the way to a study of interaction between mitochondria of different genetic types in hybrid diploid cells (see *mi* mutants of *Neurospora*, p. 95) and their segregational patterns in sexual progeny (see p. 107).

The most important aspect of the work with these antibiotics and resistant mutants relates to the mechanism of resistance. Clearly an answer to the question of what has been altered in the protein-synthesizing system of the mitochondrion that renders it largely insensitive to drug action would provide information as to which parts of the system are determined by nuclear genes and which by the mitochondrial DNA. This will require at least a detailed analysis of mitochondrial systems *in vitro*, although spectrophotometry of intact cells can provide preliminary information. For example, in certain gene-resistant mutants resistance is reflected in an altered pattern of cytochromes.

Attempts were made in the case of the two cytoplasmic mutants to find the mechanism of resistance, adopting the working hypothesis that the mutant mitochondrial DNA makes altered structural protein of the inner membrane such that it constitutes a permeability barrier to erythromycin. To test this hypothesis, both anaerobically grown and glucose-repressed cells of the two strains were put down on media containing the drug under conditions inducing respiration. Since these cells have no inner mitochondrial membrane and probably no organized outer membrane in anaerobic cells to begin with, loss of resistance would have confirmed the hypothesis while the manifestation of resistance would indicate that permeability was not a factor. Although resistance was shown by the cells under the conditions of the experiment and the latter deduction adopted, this does not rule out the possibility of resistance being due to alteration in membrane structure but it appears much more likely that alteration in the protein-synthesizing system is the answer. Anaerobically grown cells of a gene-resistant strain were also tested in these experiments and were found to be sensitive to erythromycin, implicating mitochondrial membrane (presumably inner membrane) in the resistance. This leads to the hypothesis that all gene-resistant mutants have altered inner membrane since the synthesis of this assembly is sensitive to the drug.

Studies with cycloheximide. Chloramphenicol and erythromycin inhibit protein synthesis in bacteria by binding to the bacterial ribosome which is of the 70 S type (Vasquez, 1966; Tanaka *et al.*, 1966; Taubman *et al.*, 1966). It has been suggested by Linnane that these antibiotics may block protein synthesis in mytochondria in the same way by specifically binding to a mitochondrial 'ribosome' with properties similar to the bacterial unit. The existence of mitochondrial ribosomes is likely as there are several reports of sedimenting RNA particles in mitochondrial fractions (see Chapter One). To emphasize the distinction between the mitochondrial protein-synthesizing system and that of the general system of the cell based on the 80 S ribosome, Clark-Walker and Linnane (1966) investigated the effect of cycloheximide on the synthesis of cytochromes in *S. cerevisiae*. This antibiotic is a potent inhibitor of protein synthesis in eucaryotic cells, but has no inhibitory effects on bacterial cells or on bacterial protein-synthesizing systems *in vitro*. Using a low concentration of cycloheximide that inhibited the growth rate (i.e. the microsomal protein synthesis rate) by approximately half that of the control, it was found that the formation of cytochromes *a* and a_3 was not preferentially affected. From these results the conclusion seemed well founded that the yeast cell has two protein-synthesizing systems, one cytoplasmic and the other mitochondrial, and that they are distinguishable one from the other, on the basis of differential sensitivity to antibiotics.

An extension of this investigation with cycloheximide has been carried out (Wilkie, 1967) using resistant strains of *S. cerevisiae* that can grow in the presence of comparatively large amounts of the antibiotic. The suitability of these strains for this work lies in the fact that the mechanism of resistance has been worked out (Cooper, Banthorpe, and Wilkie, 1967). In strains carrying recessive nuclear genes conferring resistance the mechanism is by way of altered ribosomes, that is, of the 80 S type. Dominant genes for resistance do not affect the ribosomes but may function to inactivate the cycloheximide. One of the *in vitro* microsomal systems used in these studies was incidentally tested for chloramphenicol effects and found to be unaffected by the presence of this drug.

Several cycloheximide-resistant strains were used, including a mutant resistant to 1 mg/ml, and all carried recessive genes for resistance. Appropriate concentrations of the antibiotic were used up to 500 μg/ml in the case of the high-level resistant strain. It was found that all strains were able to grow in glycerol-drug medium indicating that a respiratory system was being synthesized under these conditions, and all cultures showed the presence of normal relative amounts of cytochromes *a*, *b*, and *c*. The only difference between cells grown in the presence of the antibiotic and the controls was in the overall amounts of cytochrome per cell. In the presence of cycloheximide only about half of the quantities of cytochromes per cell was produced compared with control cells grown in the absence of the drug. Nevertheless, these results fully substantiate those of Linnane and his associates and show no inhibition by cycloheximide of the synthesis of cytochromes *a* and *b*, that is, there is apparent insensitivity of the protein-synthesizing system of the mitochondrion to the action of this drug.

Further supporting evidence for these findings has come from preliminary *in vitro* studies. Using a mitochondrial preparation of another facultative anaerobic yeast, *S. carlsbergensis*, Grivell (unpublished results) found that cycloheximide at a concentration of 500 μg/ml had no effect on the incorporation of labelled amino acid into mitochondrial protein, although this yeast is sensitive to 1 μg/ml of the antibiotic *in vivo*.

These results emphasize the specific activity of the antibacterial antibiotics on the mitochondrial system, or to be more precise, on that aspect of the system controlling the synthesis of cytochromes *a* and *b*.

The two categories of antibiotic, cycloheximide, on the one hand, and the bacterial ones, on the other, clearly pinpoint discrete differences in the mitochondrial and cytoplasmic systems respectively, but tell us virtually nothing about these differences in biochemical terms. The opportunity of resolving some of these differences in yeast is provided by resistant mutants, the study of which opens up a new approach to the problem.

Discussion and conclusions on the mitochondrial system in yeast
There are obvious selective advantages for the cell in being able to dispense with its mitochondrial system in appropriate circumstances. To do this has required the evolution both of a mechanism of repression and of a system ensuring the transmission of mitochondrial genetic information while the organelle has undergone disintegration. In the petite-positive yeasts there appears to be an inherent weakness in the overall system of mitochondrial reproduction in that the mitochondrial DNA is effectively lost with a relatively high frequency. This may be an unavoidable consequence of adaptation to the condition of the facultative anaerobe. However, the petite condition is not without some compensation, since it has been demonstrated that the respiratory mutant has a selective advantage over normal cells in a medium containing cobalt (Horn and Wilkie, 1966).

Investigation of the *gi* mutant and of mutants resistant to petite induction by acriflavin is aimed at providing information on the stability, transmission, and replication of the mitochondrial genetic unit in yeast. Work in this field probably applies only to yeast species that are facultative anaerobes, and extrapolating results to other organisms is likely to be misleading.

However, the question of the synthesis of cytochromes is fundamental to all organisms whether facultative anaerobes or obligate aerobes. There can be no doubt that the synthesis of cytochrome c is under the direct control of nuclear genes and is mediated through the cytoplasmic system based on the 80 S ribosome. It is also clear from the results with the different antibiotics that the a and b cytochromes are synthesized by a different system to that for cytochrome c. This other system is the mitochondrial one based on a postulated bacterial-type ribosome translating messages into polypeptide. That the mitochondrial DNA carries enough information to specify the complete inner membrane assembly is a possibility, provided no other demands are made of it, such as the specifying of the components of the protein-synthesizing machinery of the organelle. On the other hand, the cases of cytoplasmic resistance to erythromycin suggest some involvement in the latter process. Indeed, providing messenger RNA can get into the mitochondrion, it becomes an attractive hypothesis that the role of the mitochondrial DNA is to specify mitochondrial ribosomes, that is, ribosomal RNA and ribosomal proteins (see p. 51), and that the majority of other mitochondrial proteins are specified by nuclear genes.

It is of further interest in the evolution of the mitochondrial system that genetic recombination between differently marked MDNA has been found in the authors' laboratory. In crosses between ρ factor mutants resistant to erythromycin and paromomycin respectively, double-resistant and double-sensitive recombinant diploids have been obtained with high frequency.

Linnane's group working independently with related erythromycin-resistant mutants also report ρ factor involvement in resistance and coupled to non-Mendelian inheritance (personal communication and Bari symposium, 1967). It is likely that most of the conclusions reached here have now been independently arrived at by Linnane's workers.

Summary and Conclusions

Because the prospect of new and important results is so certain it would be foolhardy at this time to make rigid pronouncements as to the mechanism of synthesis. First, we must be cautious not to assume that the findings with one type of cell are of relevance to another. Not all cells are facultative anaerobes, for example, nor is the respiratory system of *Neurospora crassa* necessarily typical of all obligate aerobes. We feel, therefore, that the safest approach at this stage is to summarize the essential findings and to indicate the areas of uncertainty.

The work on mitochondrial nucleic acids and protein synthesis establishes with certainty that the mitochondrion has some sort of system of self-replication. There is no doubt at all that mitochondria contain DNA, and that this DNA is distinct from nuclear DNA. They also appear to contain a DNA polymerase, and hence are capable of replicating any genetic information in the DNA. RNA polymerase is also present, and as the enzyme appears to be DNA-dependent, the means of transcription of this information is available. There is also little doubt that mitochondria contain a full complement of activating enzymes, transfer RNA molecules, and other co-factors for protein synthesis. Recent evidence also makes it very likely that they contain characteristic ribosomes. Thus the machinery for the third major process, translation of the genetic message, is also present. The experiments on amino-acid incorporation with isolated mitochondria fully confirm all these indications, and show that mitochondria can indeed take up amino acids into the interior of the peptide chain. The protein synthesis system is relatively autonomous and is active in quite simple media. It is very closely associated with the energy-yielding apparatus of the mitochondrion, and responds to quite subtle changes in mitochondrial structure and metabolism. Thus mitochondria have many properties in common with bacteria, and indeed it is not surprising that bacterial contamination is an ever-present hazard in experiments on the bio-synthetic activities of isolated mitochondria.

Experiments in the living cell with radioactive tracers confirm these views. Labelling with lipid, protein, and nucleic-acid precursors all show that there is apparent continuity in the mitochondrial substance from one generation to the next. The results suggest that mitochondria arise by growth and division, and that mitochondrial replication can proceed continuously throughout the cell cycle. Cytological evidence also shows that mitochondria can fuse, elongate, divide, and undergo rapid and apparently independent changes in size and shape.

On the basis of such results, one would imagine that it was now firmly established that the mitochondrion is nothing more or less than an intra-cellular micro-organism, with some sort of symbiotic relationship to the host cell. We have seen in Chapter Four that it is indeed quite possible to construct a plausible theory of mitochondrial evolution based on the idea of 'endosymbiosis'. Other evidence suggests that the matter is not quite so simple, however. The DNA in the mitochondrion appears to be somewhat more homogeneous than nuclear DNA, and has a very limited coding capacity, possibly only enough for thirty proteins, which is far less than the amount required for the total synthesis of a mito-chondrion. Although mitochondria can synthesize lipids, it is far from certain whether all the mitochondrial lipids are synthesized in the mito-chondrion. At the moment we know very little as to the site of synthesis of mitochondrial transfer RNA's and ribosomes, and it is not known whether they are made on mitochondrial DNA. If they were, they would use up much of the informational content of the DNA. Most disturbing of all to the simple 'self-replication' theory, mitochondria do not appear to synthesize soluble proteins. In the particular case of cytochrome c we now have very good evidence in the case of rat liver that the protein is made in the endoplasmic reticulum and transferred to the mitochon-drion by some means. In the case of yeast, information is in nuclear genes. The actual protein synthesized by the mitochondrion appears to be insoluble membrane protein, probably involved in membrane assembly and devoid of enzyme activity.

Much cytological evidence also favours the view that mitochondria arise by differentiation of 'promitochondrial membranes' which can

H

appear in various parts of the cell, including the vicinity of the nuclear membrane. Experiments with yeast show mitochondria being formed near to, or from, vesicular structures, and it should not be forgotten that the anaerobic cell is apparently devoid of discrete mitochondria, and yet on admission of oxygen normal mitochondria are elaborated. We thus have good evidence that the biosynthetic activity of the mitochondrion is limited, and that non-mitochondrial structures are involved in mitochondrial formation.

It is well established, mainly from work with yeast, that mitochondrial formation is regulated not only by information in the mitochondrion itself but to an important extent by nuclear genes. Results from yeast also indicate that the assembly of only the inner membrane is under the control of mitochondrial DNA. Whether the latter codes directly for all the proteins of the inner membrane, for only the structural or 'organizer' proteins or for the system that mediates the translation of genetic messages coming from elsewhere, is a crucial point as yet unresolved.

The final picture is of an organelle of limited self-reproductive capacity. The work with antibiotics provides one of the main clues in distinguishing the contribution to the final process of mitochondrial assembly of the biosynthetic activities of the mitochondrion from those of the rest of the cell. The non-mitochondrial systems are much involved, and seem to provide 'pre-cast' units, or building blocks. How all the building blocks, pre-cast or made *in situ*, are fitted together to make the final functional structure remains a central problem. Another important question is how the activities of the nucleus, cytoplasmic ribosomes, and the biosynthetic system of the mitochondrion itself are co-ordinated. The knowledge gained in recent years, the main features of which form the basis of this text, has served to put these problems in clearer perspective.

References

ADAMS, E. C. and HERTIG, A. T. (1964). *J. Cell Biol.* **21**, 397.

ANDRÉ, J. and MARINOZZI, V. (1965). *J. Microscopie*, **4**, 615.

ASAKURA, S. and EGUCHI, G. (1964). *J. molec. Biol.* **10**, 42.

AVERS, C. J., RANCOURT, M. W., and LIN, F. H. (1965). *Proc. Natn. Acad. Sci. U.S.A.*, **54**, 527.

BADE, E. G. (1964). *Z. Zellforsch.* **61**, 754.

BAHR, G. F. and ZEITLER, E. (1962). *J. Cell Biol.* **15**, 489.

BAILEY, E., TAYLOR, C. B., and BARTLEY, W. (1967). *Biochem. J.* **104**, 1026.

BARNETT, W. E. and BROWN, D. H. (1967). *Proc. Natn. Acad. Sci. U.S.A.* **57**, 452.

BARNETT, W. E., BROWN, D. H., and EPLER, J. L. (1967). *Proc. Natn. Acad. Sci. U.S.A.* **57**, 1775.

BARTLEY, W. and TUSTANOFF, E. F. (1966) *Biochem. J.* **99**, 599.

BEATTIE, D. S., BASFORD, R. E., and KORITZ, S. B. (1966). *Biochemistry*, **5**, 926.

BEATTIE, D. S., BASFORD, R. E., and KORITZ, S. B. (1967). *J. biol. Chem.* **242**, 3366.

BELL, P. R. and MÜHLETHALER, K. (1962). *J. Ultrastruct. Res.* **7**, 452.

BERG, W. E. and HUMPHREYS, W. J. (1960). *Devel. Biol.* **2**, 42.

BERGER, E. R. (1964). *J. Ultrastruct. Res.* **11**, 90.

BORST, P. and RUTTENBERG, G. J. C. M. (1966). *Biochim. biophys. Acta*, **114**, 645.

BORST, P., KROON, A. M., and RUTTENBERG, G. J. C. M. (1967). In *Genetic Elements: Properties and Function*. Ed. D. Shuger, Academic Press and P. W. N., London and Warsaw, pp. 81–116.

BRAUN, G. A., MARSH, J. B., and DRABKIN, D. L. (1963). *Biochim. biophys. Acta*, **72**, 647.

BRETTHAUER, R. K., MARCUS, L., CHALOUPKA, J., HALVORSON, H. O., and BOCK, R. M. (1963). *Biochemistry*, **2**, 1079.

BRONK, J. R. (1963). *Proc. Natn. Acad. Sci. U.S.A.* **50**, 524.

BRONSERT, U. and NEUPERT, W. (1966). In *Regulation of Metabolic Processes in Mitochondria*. Ed. J. M. Tager, S. Papa, E. Quagliariello, and E. C. Slater, Elsevier, Amsterdam, pp. 426–37.

BROSEMER, R. W., VOGELL, W., and BÜCHER, TH. (1963). *Bioch. Z.* **338**, 854.

BÜCHER, TH. (1965). *Biochem. Soc. Symp.* **25**, 15.

BULDER, C. J. E. A. (1964). *Antonie van Leeuwenhoek*, **30**, 1.

BURGOYNE, L. A. and SYMONS, R. H. (1966). *Biochim. biophys. Acta*, **129**, 502.

CAMPBELL, M. K., MAHLER, H. R., MOORE, W. J., and TEWARI, S. (1966). *Biochemistry*, **5**, 1174.

CHÈVREMONT, M., BASSLEER, R., and BAECKELAND, E. (1961). *Arch. Biol. (Liège)*, **72**, 501.

CLARK-WALKER, D. G. and LINNANE, A. W. (1966). *Biochem. biophys. Res. Comm.* **25**, 8.

COOPER, D., BANTHORPE, D. V., and WILKIE, D. (1967). *J. molec. Biol.* **26**, 347.

CORNEO, G., MOORE, C., SANADI, D. R., GROSSMAN, L. I., and MARMUR, J. (1966). *Science*, **151**, 687.

CRABTREE, H. G. (1929). *Biochem. J.* **23**, 536.

CRADDOCK, V. M. and SIMPSON, M. V. (1961). *Biochem. J.* **80**, 348.

CRIDDLE, R. S., BOCK, R. M., GREEN, D. E., and TISDALE, H. (1962). *Biochemistry*, **1**, 827.

CRIDDLE, R. S., EDWARDS, D. L., and PETERSEN, T. G. (1966). *Biochemistry*, **5**, 578.

CUMMINS, J. E., RUSCH, H. P., and EVANS, T. E. (1967). *J. molec. Biol.* **23**, 281.

CUZNER, M. L., DAVISON, A. N., and GREGSON, N. A. (1966). *Biochem. J.* **101**, 618.

DADOUNE, J. P. (1963). *Archs. Anat. microsc. Morph. exp.* **52**, 513.

DAVIES, J. W. and COCKING, E. C. (1967). *Biochem. J.* **104**, 23.

DAWID, I. B. (1966). *Proc. Natn. Acad. Sci. U.S.A.* **56**, 269.

DEJGIE, D. S., BATTAD, L. E., and KNITZ, F. B. (1967). *J. biol. Chem.* **242**, 3366.

De DEKEN, R. H. (1961). *Expl. Cell Res.* **24**, 145.

De DEKEN, R. H. (1966). *J. gen. Microbiol.* **44**, 149, 157.

DEUCHAR, E. M. (1966). *Biochemical Aspects of Amphibian Development.* Methuen, London.

DIACUMAKOS, E. G., GARNJOBST, L., and TATUM, E. L. (1965). *J. Cell Biol.* **26**, 427.

DROZ, B. and BERGERON, M. (1965). *C. Rend. Acad. Sci.* Paris, **261**, 2757.

DU BUY, H. G. and RILEY, F. L. (1967). *Proc. Natn. Acad. Sci. U.S.A.* **57**, 790.

DU BUY, H. G., MATTERN, C. F. T., and RILEY, F. L. (1966). *Biochim. biophys. Acta*, **123**, 298.

DUVE, C. de (1967). In *Enzyme Cytology*, Ed. D. B. Roodyn, Academic Press, London.

DUVE, C. de and BAUDHUIN, P. (1966). *Physiol. Rev.* **46**, 232.

EISENSTADT, J. M. and BRAWERMAN, G. (1964). *J. molec. Biol.* **10**, 392.

ELAEV, I. R. (1967). *Biokhimiya*, **31**, 234.

ELSON, D. (1967). In *Enzyme Cytology*. Ed. D. B. Roodyn, Academic Press, London, pp. 407-73.

EPHRUSSI, B. (1950). *Harvey Lect.* **46**, 45.

EPHRUSSI, B. (1953). *Nucleo-cytoplasmic relations in microorganisms.* Clarendon Press, Oxford.

EPHRUSSI, B. and GRANDCHAMP, S. (1965). *Heredity, Lond.* **20**, 1.

EPHRUSSI, B. and HOTTINGUER, H. (1951). *Cold Spring Harb. Symp. quant. Biol.* **16**, 75.

EPHRUSSI, B. and SLONIMSKI, P. P. (1950). *Biochim. biophys. Acta*, **6**, 256.

EPHRUSSI, B., HOTTINGUER, H., and ROMAN, H. (1955). *Proc. Natn. Acad. Sci. U.S.A.* **41**, 1065.

EPHRUSSI, B., JAKOB, H., and GRANDCHAMP, S. (1966). *Genetics, Princeton*, **54**, 1.

EPHRUSSI, B., SLONIMSKI, P. P., YOTSUYANAGI, Y., and TAVLIZKI, J. (1956). *C. r. Trav. Lab. Carlsberg*, **26**, 87.

FAWCETT, D. W. (1955). *J. Natn. Cancer Inst.* **15**, 1475.

FLETCHER, M. J. and SANADI, D. R. (1961). *Biochim. biophys. Acta*, **51**, 356.

FREDERIC, J. (1958). *Arch. Biol. (Liège)* **69**, 167.

FREEMAN, K. B., ROODYN, D. B., and TATA, J. R. (1963). *Biochim. biophys. Acta*, **72**, 129.

FUKUHARA, H. (1967). *Biochim. biophys. Acta*, **134**, 143.

FUKUHARA, H. and SELS, A. (1966). *J. molec. Biol.* **17**, 319.

GAHAN, P. B. and CHAYEN, J. (1965). *Int. Rev. Cytol.* **18**, 223.

GARFINKEL, D. (1963). *J. biol. Chem.* **238**, 2440.

GIBOR, A. and GRANICK, S. (1964). *Science*, **145**, 890.

GNANAM, A. and KAHN, J. S. (1967). *Biochim. biophys. Acta*, **142**, 486.

GONZÁLEZ-CADAVID, N. F. and CAMPBELL, P. N. (1967). *Biochem. J.* **105**, 443.

GREEN, D. E. and HECHTER, O. (1965). *Proc. Natn. Acad. Sci. U.S.A.* **53**, 318.

GRIVELL, L. A. (1967). *Biochem. J.* (In press.)

GUSTAFSSON, R., TATA, J. R., LINDBERG, O., and ERNSTER, L. (1965). *J. Cell Biol.* **26**, 555.

GUTTES, E. W., HANAWALT, P. C., and GUTTES, S. (1967). *Biochim. biophys. Acta*, **142**, 181.

HALDAR, D., FREEMAN, K., and WORK, T. S. (1966). *Nature, Lond.* **211**, 9.

HALDAR, D., FREEMAN, K. B., and WORK, T. S. (1967). *Biochem. J.* **102**, 684.

HARTMAN, J. F. (1954). *Anat. Rec.* **118**, 19.

HORN, P. (1965). Ph.D. Thesis, University of London.

HORN, P. and WILKIE, D. (1966). *Heredity, Lond.* **21**, 625.

HUANG, M., BIGGS, D. R., CLARK-WALKER, D. G., and LINNANE, A. W. (1966). *Biochim. biophys. Acta*, **114**, 434.

HUMM, D. G. and HUMM, J. H. (1966). *Proc. Natn. Acad. Sci. U.S.A.* **55**, 114.

ISRAEL, J. V., ANDERSON, T. F., and LEVINE, M. (1967). *Proc. Natn. Acad. Sci. U.S.A.* **57**, 284.

JAKOB, H. (1965). *Genetics, Princeton*, **52**, 75.

JAYARAMAN, J., COTMAN, C., MAHLER, H. R., and SHARP, C. W. (1966). *Archs. Biochem. Biophys.* **116**, 224.

KADENBACH, B. (1967a). *Biochim. biophys. Acta*, **134**, 430.

KADENBACH, B. (1967b). *Biochim. biophys. Acta*, **138**, 651.

KAHN, V. and BLUM, J. J. (1967). *Biochemistry*, **6**, 817.

KALF, G. F. (1963). *Archs. Biochem. Biophys.* **101**, 350.

KALF, G. F. (1964). *Biochemistry*, **3**, 1702.

KALF, G. F. and GRÉCE, M. A. (1966). *J. biol. Chem.* **241**, 1019.

KATOH, T. and SANUKIDA, S. (1965). *Bioch. biophys. Res. Comm.* **21**, 373.

KROON, A. M. (1963a). *Biochim. biophys. Acta*, **76**, 165.

KROON, A. M. (1963b). *Biochim. biophys. Acta*, **72**, 391.

KROON, A. M. (1964). *Biochim. biophys. Acta*, **91**, 145.

KROON, A. M. (1965). *Biochim. biophys. Acta*, **108**, 275.

KROON, A. M. (1966a). In *Regulation and Metabolic Processes in Mitochondria*. Ed. J. M. Tager, S. Papa, E. Quagliariello, and E. C. Slater, Elsevier, Amsterdam, pp. 396–414.

KROON, A. M. (1966b). Ph.D. Thesis, University of Amsterdam.

KROON, A. M., BORST, P., VAN BRUGGEN, E. F. J., and RUTTENBERG, G. J. C. M. (1966). *Proc. Natn. Acad. Sci. U.S.A.* **56**, 1836.

KROON, A. M., SACCONE, C., and BOTMAN, M. J. (1967). *Biochim. biophys. Acta*, **142**, 552.

LADO, P. and SCHWENDIMANN, M. (1967). *Ital. J. Biochem.* **15**, 279.

LASCELLES, J. (1966). In *15th Symposium of Society of General Microbiology*, pp. 32–56.

LEHNINGER, A. L. (1964). *The Mitochondrion*. W. A. Benjamin Inc., New York.

LEMOIGNE, M., AUBERT, J. P., and MILLET, J. (1954). *Annls. Inst. Pasteur, Paris*, **87**, 427.

LERMAN, L. S. (1963). *Proc. Natn. Acad. Sci. U.S.A.* **49**, 94.

LINDENMAYER, A. and ESTABROOK, R. W. (1958). *Archs. Biochem. Biophys.* **78**, 66.

LINNANE, A. W., VITOLS, E., and NOWLAND, P. G. (1962). *J. Cell Biol.* **13**, 345.

LUCK, D. J. L. (1963). *J. Cell Biol.* **16**, 483.

LUCK, D. J. L. (1965). *J. Cell Biol.* **24**, 445.

LUCK, D. J. L. and REICH, E. (1964). *Proc. Natn. Acad. Sci. U.S.A.* **52**, 931.

LUCY, J. A. and GLAUERT, A. M. (1964). *J. molec. Biol.* **8**, 727.

MAGER, J. (1960). *Biochim. biophys. Acta*, **38**, 150.

MALTZAHN, K. von and MÜHLETHALER, K. (1962). Experientia, **18**, 315.

MARGOLIASH, E. (1963). *Proc. Natn. Acad. Sci. U.S.A.* **50**, 672.

MATTOON, J. R. and SHERMAN, F. (1966). *J. biol. Chem.* **241**, 4330.

MCCLARY, D. O. and BOWERS, W. D. (1967). *J. Cell Biol.* **32**, 519.

MCLEAN, J. R., COHN, G. L., BRANDT, I. K., and SIMPSON, M. V. (1958). *J. biol. Chem.* **233**, 657.

MESELSON, M. and STAHL, F. W. (1958). *Proc. Natn. Acad. Sci. U.S.A.* **44**, 671.

MITCHELL, H. K. and MITCHELL, M. B. (1952). *Proc. Natn. Acad. Sci. U.S.A.* **38**, 442.

MITCHELL, H. K. and MITCHELL, M. B. (1956). *J. gen. microbiol.* **14**, 184.

MOUNOLOU, J. C., JAKOB, H., and SLONIMSKI, P. P. (1966). *Biochem. biophys. Res. Comm.* **24**, 218.

MOUSTACCHI, E. and WILLIAMSON, D. H. (1966). *Biochem. biophys. Res. Comm.* **23**, 56.

MUGNAINI, E. (1964a). *J. Cell Biol.* **23**, 173.

MUGNAINI, E. (1964b). *J. Ultrastruct. Res.* **11**, 525.

MUNKRES, K. D. and WOODWARD, D. O. (1966). *Proc. Natn. Acad. Sci. U.S.A.* **55**, 1217.

NASS, M. M. K. (1966). *Proc. Natn. Acad. Sci. U.S.A.* **56**, 1215.

NASS, S. and NASS, M. M. K. (1963). *J. R. microsc. Soc.* **81**, 209.

NASS, M. M. K., NASS, S., and AFZELIUS, B. A. (1965). *Expl. Cell Res.* **37**, 516.

NATHANS, D. (1964). *Proc. Natn. Acad. Sci. U.S.A.* **51**, 585.

NEGROTTI, T. and WILKIE, D. (1967). *Biochim. biophys. Acta.* (In press.)

NEUBERT, D. and HELGE, H. (1965). *Biochem. biophys. Res. Comm.* **18**, 600.

NEUBERT, D., HELGE, H., and BASS, R. (1965). *Arch. exp. Path. Pharmak.* **252**, 258.

NEUBERT, D., HELGE, H., and MERKER, H. J. (1965). *Biochem. Z.* **343**, 44.

NEUPERT, W., BRDICZKA, D., and BÜCHER, TH. (1967). *Biochem. biophys. Res. Comm.* **27**, 488.

NORTH, R. J. and POLLAK, J. K. (1961). *J. Ultrastruct. Res.* **5**, 497.

NOVIKOFF, A. B. (1961). In *The Cell, Vol. II.* Ed. J. Brachet and A. E. Mirsky, Academic Press, New York, pp. 299–422.

NOVIKOFF, A. B. and ESSNER, E. (1962). *J. Cell Biol.* **15**, 140.

O'BRIEN, T. W. and KALF, G. F. (1967). *J. biol. Chem.* **242**, 2172.

OLSON, M. S. and VON KORFF, R. W. (1967). *J. biol. Chem.* **242**, 325.

PARSONS, J. A. (1965). *J. Cell. Biol.* **25**, 641.

PARTHIER, B. (1963). *Biochim. biophys. Acta*, **72**, 503.

PITTINGER, T. H. (1956). *Proc. Natn. Acad. Sci. U.S.A.* **42**, 747.

POLAKIS, E. S., BARTLEY, W., and MEEK, G. A. (1964). *Biochem. J.* **90**, 369.

POLAKIS, E. S., BARTLEY, W., and MEEK, G. A. (1965). *Biochem. J.* **97**, 298.

PETERMANN, M. L. (1964). *The Physical and Chemical Properties of Ribosomes.* Elsevier, Amsterdam.

RABINOWITZ, M., DE SALLE, L., SINCLAIR, J., STIREWALT, R., and SWIFT, H. (1966). *Fed. Proc.* **25**, 581.

RACKER, E. (1962). Proc. *Natn. Acad. Sci. U.S.A.* **48**, 1659.

RAZIN, S., MOROWITZ, H. J., and TERRY, T. M. (1964). *Proc. Natn. Acad. Sci. U.S.A.* **54**, 219.

REICH, E. and LUCK, D. J. L. (1966). *Proc. Natn. Acad. Sci. U.S.A.* **55**, 1600.

REID, E. (1967). In *Enzyme Cytology.* Ed. D. B. Roodyn, Academic Press, London, pp. 321-406.

REILLY, C. and SHERMAN, F. (1965). *Biochim. biophys. Acta,* **95**, 640.

REIS, P. J., COOTE, J. L., and WORK, T. S. (1959). Nature, Lond. **184**, 165.

RICHARDSON, J. P. (1966). *J. molec. Biol.* **21**, 83.

RICHARDSON, J. H., HULTIN, H. O., and FLEISCHER, S. (1964). *Archs. Biochem. Biophys.* **105**, 254.

RITCHIE, D. and HAZELTINE, P. (1953). *Expl. Cell Res.* **5**, 261.

RIVA, S. C. (1966). *Biochem. biophys. Res. Comm.* **23**, 606.

ROBERTIS, E. de and BLEICHMAR, H. (1962). *Z. Zellforsch.* **57**, 572.

ROBERTSON, J. D. (1959). *Biochem. Soc. Symp.* **16**, 3.

ROGERS, P. J., PRESTON, B. N., TITCHENER, E. B., and LINNANE, A. W. (1967). *Biochem. biophys. Res. Comm.* **27**, 405.

ROODYN, D. B. (1962). *Biochem. J.* **85**, 177.

ROODYN, D. B. (1965). *Biochem. J.* **97**, 782.

ROODYN, D. B. (1966a). In *Regulation of Metabolic Processes in Metachondria,* Ed. J. M. Tager, S. Papa, E. Quagliariello, and E. L. Slater. (BBA Library, Vol. 7). Elsevier, Amsterdam, pp. 383-96.

ROODYN, D. B. (1966b). In *Regulation of Metabolic Processes in Mitochondria.* Ed. J. M. Tager, S. Papa, E. Quagliariello, and E. C. Slater, Elsevier, Amsterdam, pp. 562-63.

ROODYN, D. B. (1967). In *Enzyme Cytology.* Ed. D. B. Roodyn, Academic Press, London, pp. 103-80.

ROODYN, D. B. and WILKIE, D. (1966). *Biochem. J.* **103**, 3c.

ROODYN, D. B., FREEMAN, K. B., and TATA, J. R. (1965). *Biochem. J.* **94**, 628.

ROODYN, D. B., REIS, P. J., and WORK, T. S. (1961). *Biochem. J.* **80**, 9.

ROODYN, D. B., SUTTIE, J. W., and WORK, T. S. (1962). *Biochem. J.* **83**, 29.

ROUILLER, C., and BERNHARD, W. (1956). *J. biophys. biochem. Cytol. Suppl.* **2**, 355.

SACCONE, C., GADALETA, M. N., and QUAGLIARIELLO, E. (1967). *Biochim. biophys. Acta,* **138**, 474.

SAGAN, L. (1967). *J. theor. Biol.* **14**, 225.

SANDELL, S., LÖW, H., and der DECKEN, A. (1967). *Biochem. J.* **104**, 575.

SCHATZ, G. (1965). *Biochim. biophys. Acta*, **96**, 342.

SCHJEIDE, O. A., MCCANDLESS, R. G., and MUNN, R. J. (1964). *Nature*, Lond. **203**, 158.

SCHUSTER, F. L. (1965). *Expl. Cell Res.* **39**, 329.

SHERMAN, F. (1963). *Genetics, Princeton*, **48**, 375.

SHERMAN, F. (1964). *Genetics, Princeton*, **49**, 39.

SHERMAN, F. and SLONIMSKI, P. P. (1964). *Biochim. biophys. Acta*, **91**, 1.

SHERMAN, F., STEWART, J. W., MARGOLIASH, E., PARKER, J., and CAMPBELL, W. (1966). *Proc. Natn. Acad. Sci. U.S.A.* **55**, 1498.

SHIPP, W. S., KIERAS, F. J., and HASELKORN, R. (1965). *Proc. Natn. Acad. Sci. U.S.A.* **54**, 207.

SILAGI, S. (1965). *Genetics, Princeton*, **52**, 341.

SIMPSON, M. V., FOURNIER, M. J., and SKINNER, D. M. (1967). *Methods in Enzymology*, (In press.)

SIMPSON, M. V., SKINNER, D. M., and LUCAS, J. M. (1961). *J. biol. Chem.* **236**, 81.

SINCLAIR, J. H. and STEVENS, B. J. (1966). *Proc. Natn. Acad. Sci. U.S.A.* **56**, 508.

SINGER, T. P., GREGOLIN, C., and CREMONA, T. (1963). In *Control Mechanisms in Respiration and Fermentation*. Ed. B. Wright, Ronald Press Co., New York, pp. 47–79.

SISSAKIAN, N. M., FILIPPOVICH, I. I., SVETAILO, E. N., and ALIYEV, K. A. (1965). *Biochim. biophys. Acta*, **95**, 474.

SLONIMSKI, P. P. (1953). In *3rd Symp. Soc. Gen. Microbiol.* University Press, Cambridge.

SLONIMSKI, P. P. (1956). *Proc. 3rd Int. Cong. Bioch.* Academic Press, New York, p. 242.

SOMLO, M. and FUKUHARA, H. (1965). *Biochem. biophys. Res. Comm.* **19**, 587.

SOTTOCASA, G. L., KUYLENSTIERNA, B., ERNSTER, L., and BERGSTRAND, A. (1967). *J. Cell Biol.* **32**, 415.

STEINERT, M. (1960). *J. biophys. biochem. Cytol.* **8**, 542.

STUTZ, E. and NOLL, H. (1967). *Proc. Natn. Acad. Sci. U.S.A.* **57**, 774.

SUKARADA and MATSUMURA (1966). *Keijo J. Med.* **15**, 51.

SUYAMA, Y. and BONNER, W. D. (1966). *Pl. Physiol.* **41**, 383.

SWICK, R. W., STANGE, J. L., NANCE, S. L., and THOMSON, J. F. (1967). *Biochemistry*, **6**, 737.

TANAKA, K., TERASKA, H., NAGIRA, T., and TANAKI, M. (1966). *Biochim. biophys. Acta*, **123**, 435.

TATA, J. R., ERNSTER, L., LINDBERG, O., ARRHENIUS, E., PEDERSEN, S., and HEDMAN, R. (1963). *Biochem. J.* **86**, 408.

TAUBMAN, S. B., JONES, N. R., YOUNG, F. E., and CORCORAN, J. W. (1966). *Biochim. biophys. Acta,* **123**, 438.

TEWARI, K. K., VOTSCH, W., and MAHLER, H. R. (1966). *J. molec. Biol.* **20**, 453.

THOMAS, D. Y. and WILKIE, D. (1967). (In preparation.)

THOMAS, D. Y. and WILKIE, D. (1968). *Genet. Res.* (In press.)

TRUMAN, D. E. S. (1963). *Expl. Cell Res.* **31**, 313.

TRUMAN, D. E. S. and KORNER, A. (1962). *Biochem. J.* **83**, 588.

TRUMAN, D. E. S. and LÖW, H. (1963). *Expl. Cell Res.* **31**, 230.

TUSTANOFF, E. R. and BARTLEY, W. (1964). *Biochem. J.* **91**, 595.

TZAGOLOFF, A., MACLENNAN, D. H., MCCONNELL, D. G., and GREEN, D. E. (1967). *J. biol. Chem.* **242**, 2051.

VASQUEZ, D. (1966). *Biochim. biophys. Acta,* **114**, 277.

VICKERMAN, K. (1963). *Proc. Linn. Soc. Lond.* **174**, 46.

Von EHRENSTEIN, G. and LIPMANN, F. (1961). *Proc. Natn. Acad. Sci. U.S.A.* **47**, 941.

WAGNER, R. P. and MITCHELL, H. K. (1964). *Genetics and Metabolism.* Wiley, New York.

WALLACE, P. G. and LINNANE, A. W. (1964). *Nature, Lond.* **201**, 1191.

WHEELDON, L. (1966). *Biochem. biophys. Res. Comm.* **24**, 407.

WHEELDON, L. W. and LEHNINGER, A. L. (1966). *Biochemistry,* **5**, 3533.

WIDNELL, C. C. and TATA, J. R. (1966). *Biochem. J.* **98**, 621.

WILKIE, D. (1963). *J. molec. Biol.* **7**, 527.

WILKIE, D. (1964). *The Cytoplasm in Heredity.* Methuen, London.

WILKIE, D. (1967). In *Biochemical Aspects of the Biogenesis of Mitochondria.* Adriatica Editrice, Bari. (In press.)

WILKIE, D. and NEGROTTI, T. (1967). In *2nd Interntl. Yeast Congr.* Bratislava.

WILKIE, D., SAUNDERS, G. W., and LINNANE, A. W. (1967). *Genet. Res.* **10**, 105.

WILKIE, D., THOMAS, D. Y., SAUNDERS, G. W., and LINNANE, A. W. (1967). (In preparation.)

WINTERSBERGER, E. (1964). *Hoppe-Seyler's Z. physiol. Chem.* **336**, 285.

WINTERSBERGER, E. (1965). *Biochem. Z.* **341**, 409.

WINTERSBERGER, E. (1966a). *Biochem. biophys. Res. Comm.* **25**, 1.

WINTERSBERGER, E. (1966b). In *Regulation of Metabolic Processes in Mitochondria.* Ed. J. M. Tager, S. Papa, E. Quagliariello, and E. C. Slater, Elsevier, Amsterdam, pp. 439–53.

WINTERSBERGER, E. (1966c). *Allg. Probt. Chem.* **17**, 590, and 595.

WOODWARD, D. O. and MUNKRES, K. D. (1966). *Proc. Natn. Acad. Sci. U.S.A.* **55**, 872.

WORK, T. S. (1967). In *Biochemical Aspects of the Biogenesis of Mitochondria.* Adriatica Editrice, Bari. (In press.)

YCAS, M. (1956). *Expl. Cell Res.* **11**, 1.

YELLIN, T. O., BUTLER, B. J., and STEIN, H. H. (1967). *Fed. Proc.* **26**, 833.

YOTSUYANAGI, Y. (1962). *J. Ultrastruct. Res.* **7**, 121, 141.

YOTSUYANAGI, Y. (1966). *C. Rend. Acad. Sci. Paris,* **262**, 1348.

Index